Dr. Norman Hickin (1910-199(ιd
received his Ph.D. in entomolog   0.
He served as vice president of t   ιe
Institute of Biology, was a fou   fe
Artists, and was a member of mai   al
organisations. He published over   ιe
two dozen books, including Anι..... ....ρ.....,......... ....Jk,
Irish Nature, and The Natural History of an English Forest.

G000137909

THE BUTTERFLIES
of
IRELAND
A Field Guide

WRITTEN AND ILLUSTRATED BY

Dr Norman Hickin

EDITED AND INTRODUCED
BY TIM LAVERY

ROBERTS RINEHART PUBLISHERS

First published in 1992 by
Roberts Rinehart Publishers
3 Bayview Terrace
Schull, West Cork, Ireland

P.O. Box 666
121 Second Avenue
Niwot, Colorado, USA 80544

ISBN 1 879373 01 7

Library of Congress Catalog Card Number 91-065624

Cover design by Birgitta Saflund

Typesetting by Seton Graphics, Bantry, West Cork
Printed by Colour Books Ltd, Dublin

For
Miranda
my granddaughter

Lo, the bright train their radiant wings unfold.
With silver fringed, and freckled o'er with gold.
On the Gay bosom of some fragrant flower,
They idly flutt'ring live their little hour;
Their life all pleasure, and their task all play
All Spring their age, and sunshine all their day.

Anna Letitia Barbauld 1742-1825

CONTENTS

Part One

Part Two

EDITOR'S INTRODUCTION

The butterflies of Ireland have long been a source of inspiration to artists, poets and anybody interested in the creatures of the countryside.

In his book, Norman Hickin presents all the species which are permanently resident in Ireland as well as immigrants and rare visitors. Each species is dealt with in great detail throughout its lifecycle in a readable yet exact manner. Combined with this, Dr Hickin has used his extraordinary artistic talents to illustrate each stage with black and white line drawings.

It is a tragedy indeed that Norman Hickin (1910–1990) did not live to see the publication of this book on which he spent the last years of his life researching, illustrating and writing.

Never having met Norman Hickin, I came to this book as editor with considerable trepidation. However, I long knew of the author by his considerable reputation in the field of natural history, particularly in relation to Ireland, and through his many achievements in various branches of science, especially as professional entomologist, keen naturalist and artist, and in his capacity as Scientific Director of the Rentokil Group, a pest control scientist.

It is hoped that this book will serve both as an introduction to the myriad splendours which may be seen in the Irish countryside by the observant nature-lover, and as a lasting tribute to Dr Norman Hickin, a man who helped further our understanding of the world around us.

Tim Lavery

ACKNOWLEDGEMENTS

I am fortunate to have had so much help extended to me during the preparation of this book and I am especially grateful to the following:—Dr J. O'Connor of the National Museum, Dublin for the loan of specimens; Mr Raymond Haynes for help in the field and with specimens (Brimstone); Dr Tom Tolman for specimens (Brown Hairstreak) and advice about rearing techniques; Mr Bob Aldwell for specimens (Dingy Skipper); Dr Paul Hillis for help and encouragement and for reading the typescript; the late Mr Ron Bland for specimens and help in rearing (Clouded Yellow); Mrs Dorothy Bland for specimens of adults and immature stages of several species; Mr Robert Goodden in loaning specimens; Dr Martin Birch, Curator, Hope Collections, Dept of Zoology, University of Oxford, for the loan of specimens; Mrs Margaret Birch and Adam for assistance with field work; Mr Bill Clements of Florida, USA, for information on the American Painted Lady.

Due to the nature of this work there has been an immense load of secretarial work and this service, as well as the production of all the typescript, has been rendered by Pamela Gale, my personal assistant, and I am deeply grateful to her for all that she accomplished.

Grateful thanks to Mr Robin Edwards and to Rentokil Ltd. for the photographic work in connection with the colour plates.

I am grateful for the considerable help given to me by my friend Bill Johns during the final stages of the book.

Finally, I would like to thank Emma, my wife, for her companionship in the field, her encouragement whenever I flagged and for so arranging our domestic life that there was always time for the Irish Butterfly Book.

Norman Hickin

The publisher would like thank Dr J. P. O'Connor of the National Museum of Ireland and Dr M.C.D. Speight of the National Parks and Wildlife Service for their advice; Éamonn Ó hÓgáin of the Royal Irish Academy, and Colm Breathnach of the Departmant of Education for supplying the Irish names of all the butterflies; and to Tim Lavery who made publication possible by editing the manuscript and producing the maps.

INTRODUCTION

THE IMPORTANCE OF BUTTERFLIES

Why are butterflies important?

Numerically butterflies constitute a minute proportion of our total insect fauna. Including common migrants, there are only thirty-two species considered truly to be Irish. On the other hand, there are in Ireland many thousands of species of Moths, Beetles and other insects. Butterflies are, however, unique in possessing large, colourful wings in distinctive patterns and can be recognized even at a distance by most people. Extremely few species are pests. They act as signals as to climatic conditions; they can be looked upon almost as calendars as regards their dates of emergence, and their population numbers have monitored degrees of pollution and habitat change. Perhaps most important of all, they are looked upon as a vital component of the beauty of our countryside which everyone can identify and appreciate.

All the black and white illustrations in this book are produced by the scraperboard technique. The specimens of resident species and common migrants illustrated have, almost without exception, been collected in Ireland—both the adult butterflies and their immature stages as well as the food plants of the larvae. This rule has been scrupulously adhered to. Only the absolute minimum amount of 'collection' in respect of the educational value of this work was undertaken. In many cases reared butterflies were released to propagate their kind, either in their original locality or in other suitable areas, after serving as models for illustrations. Rarities were not collected, in these cases drawings were made from specimens in old collections, for example, the Small Mountain Ringlet and Monarch in the National Museum's Collections in Dublin.

Some of the rare vagrants and migrants have been illustrated from European sources—noted in the text in each case.

Compared with Europe, the Irish butterfly fauna is not rich in species but it is rich in butterfly populations and long may it remain so!

In this work the author has endeavoured to put down his own ideas on the conservation of butterflies. They may be very unpopular with butterfly collectors. They will, indeed, be much more radical in conception than the so-called voluntary rules in operation in some other countries—such as Britain—where a number of butterfly species have disappeared or nearly so in the last few years.

Most—if not all—books giving illustrations of the various life stages of butterflies show them life-size or only slightly enlarged. This often results in an absence of precise detail.

13

In the present work, however, all the figures have been drawn to approximately the same size. This means that the drawings, as reproduced, are at differing magnifications. However all actual dimensions are given.

Phrases used in the descriptions given by older writers sometimes cannot be improved. Where these have been used in the present text they are given within quotation marks.

CLASSIFICATION

Butterflies, together with the Moths, constitute the Order of Insects known as the LEPIDOPTERA. There are 27 other Orders which make up the Class INSECTA. In turn the Class INSECTA forms part of the major Group or Phylum known as the ARTHROPODA.

Within the animal kingdom ARTHROPODA is the most diverse Group and contains by far the largest in numbers of different species. It includes the Spiders, Scorpions, Ticks, Mites, Centipedes and Millipedes, Crabs, Shrimps, Lobsters and all the other Crustaceans, Horseshoe Crabs, Sea Spiders and innumerable other animals less well known.

The principal characteristic which they all share is the possession of an exoskeleton. This is a more or less horny, outer covering of the body which is segmented. Limbs are present, being jointed; also, movement and articulation are made possible by a thinning of the exoskeleton and the development of a muscular system. The function of the exoskeleton is to guard against mechanical injury and to minimise water loss. One result of the rigid nature of the exoskeleton, however, is the necessity to shed it (or moult) periodically so that growth can take place.

INSECTA, or Insects, are arthropods which possess the following characteristics:-

The body is divided into three distinct regions—head, thorax and abdomen. Antennae, mouthparts and the eyes are situated on the head. The thorax is divided into three segments, a pair of legs being borne by each. In some insect families (e.g. the Lepidoptera) the second and the third segments each bear a pair of wings, but often these segments are fused together in order to withstand the forces exerted by the flight muscles.

The abdomen consists of eleven segments but in only a few insects (at the more primitive end of the Classification) are all these visible. In the house fly, for example, only four abdominal segments can be seen.

Respiration takes place by oxygen being taken into the body through a series of apertures called 'spiracles' which are arranged along the sides of the body and which transfer the oxygen to all the tissues through a network of fine tubules known as tracheae. Carbon dioxide is expelled through the same system. Additionally, there are a number of sacs which can function as pumps, regulating the amount of gaseous exchange.

CLASSIFICATION OF INSECTS

Insects are classified first of all into two distinct groups. Those which do not possess wings are known as the APTERYGOTA, but wingless insects, (such as fleas) which have evolved from winged forms, are not included. Members of the APTERYGOTA are further characterized by the possession of leg-like appendages arising from the abdomen. No other insects show these.

All remaining insects are known as PTERYGOTA, or 'winged insects', and these are again divided into two groups. In the first are placed all those insects in which the wings develop on the outside of the body like two pairs of flaps and become successively larger at each moult of the exoskeleton. Otherwise, each immature stage (except the egg) resembles the adult except for size.

This group is known as the EXOPTERYGOTA and examples of the different Orders are ODONATA (Dragonflies), DICTYOPTERA (Cockroaches, Mantids), HEMIPTERA (Plant Bugs, Froghoppers, Water-boatmen etc.) and ORTHOPTERA (Grasshoppers, Locusts, Crickets).

In the second group, ENDOPTERYGOTA, there are distinct larval and pupal stages. The wings develop inside the body of the larva and pupa and these two stages are very different in form from that of the adult. There are nine Orders in this group, examples being COLEOPTERA (Beetles), HYMENOPTERA (Ants, Bees, Wasps etc.), DIPTERA (Two-winged flies or True flies), TRICHOPTERA (Caddisflies) and LEPIDOPTERA (Butterflies and Moths).

The wings and body of LEPIDOPTERA, or Butterflies and Moths, are covered with minute scales which overlap like the tiles on a roof, but on the body they may be hairlike, often giving the appearance of fur. The wing-scales are frequently highly pigmented and the various patterns made by them constitute not only some of the most beautiful patterns of nature but also show a number of scientific laws, for all to see, associated with inheritance, cryptic colouration, and subspeciation. The colours and patterns of the wings are a considerable aid to identification.

The functional mouthparts of Butterflies and Moths consist almost entirely of a proboscis which can be coiled like a watch spring. It is capable only of sucking up liquids such as nectar from flowers, an important source of energy for those species embarking on several months of hibernation during which food and drink are denied and activity is reduced to a very low level.

It was at one time thought that Moths and Butterflies were two very distinct groups within the LEPIDOPTERA, however, it is now thought that butterflies constitute two if not more separate entities. The following characteristics will show the differences—at least between Irish butterflies—RHOPALOCERA (Club-horned) and moths-HETEROCERA (Variously-horned).

Indeed, this is perhaps the most consistent of the ways to distinguish between Moths and Butterflies. Another difference lies in the manner in which the wings are held when the insect is at rest. With only one exception, butterflies hold their wings flat against each other over the back, the exception being the Dingy Skipper which holds them tent-wise around the body whilst extending them sideways, as do the Moths.

All butterflies (or more correctly their larvae—caterpillars) are vegetarian in their diet of leaves, flowers, buds or berries of their various food plants. Whilst some butterflies are specific in their diet, feeding on only one species of plant, others are found on a number of species, but these are usually related and belong to one Family. However, there are several exceptions, e.g. the Green Hairstreak larvae are recorded as feeding on LEGUMINOSEAE, ERICACEAE, ROSA-CEAE and species of some other plant families.

CLASSIFICATION OF IRISH BUTTERFLIES

Ireland is host to five butterfly families. This number might be increased by one if we include the Monarch butterfly (*Danaus plexippus*) which is a rare immigrant (or vagrant).

The HESPERIIDAE (Skippers) is a Family distributed worldwide and it is represented in the Irish fauna by a single species—the Dingy Skipper, *Erynnis tages*. Members of this family are characterized by an unusual 'skipping' flight, by their small size and the lack of reds, greens or blues amongst their colouration.

The PIERIDAE, or 'Whites and Yellows', are represented by six resident species, one common migrant—the Clouded Yellow—and two rare vagrants. The last three species never pass the winter in Ireland; arriving here in the Spring and early Summer, the migrant species are unable to withstand the Irish winter no matter how mild we believe it to be. The wings of the PIERIDAE are either white or yellow, often with black markings.

The eggs are tall and skittle-shaped and the larvae do not possess spines. The pupae are attached to a silken pad by a cremaster, further secured by a girdle.

The Family LYCAENIDAE, consisting of Hairstreaks, Coppers and Blues, are represented by seven species and in our Irish Butterfly List there are three each of Hairstreaks and Blues and one Copper.

The adults are usually small whilst the wings (especially those of the male) are of brilliant colouration—often shining blue or copper. The female is rather more subdued. The larvae are slug-like in shape and have a small head which can be withdrawn into the first segment of the thorax. In the

NYMPHALIDAE, of which the Fritillaries account for four, there are eight Irish species but two are immigrants—the Red Admiral and the Painted Lady. It is the largest Family of butterflies and has a worldwide distribution. The chief characteristic is the reduction in the first pair of legs of the adult so that they do not function as walking legs. In the male they are without claws but are covered with long hair and in the female a number of small spines take the place of leg-claws. The larvae have large spines along the back and the pupae hang suspended, without the support of a girdle.

There are nine Irish species in the SATYRIDAE or Browns. Some authorities consider this to be only a subdivision of the NYMPHALIDAE, but they are sufficiently distinct to merit description here.

They are usually sombre browns and yellows and the wings are decorated with eye-like marks. The front pair of legs are not used for walking. The larvae are long, tapering at the front and rear with the extreme tip of the body forked. They are green or brownish with pale, longitudinal stripes. They do not possess spines but are covered with fine hair. They all feed on grasses except one which feeds on a sedge. Some pupae are suspended by a cremaster, others lie on the ground in a loose cocoon.

THE LIFE CYCLE OF A BUTTERFLY

There are four distinct stages in the life cycle of a butterfly—egg, larva, chrysalis or pupa and the adult.

EGG (ALSO CALLED OVUM)

There is great variation in the form of butterfly eggs. A number are almost globular whilst others are tall, bottle- or skittle-shaped; yet again a number are squat, being almost disc-shaped. The nature of the surface also shows some variation. In some species the egg-shell, or chorion, is smooth or nearly so, but more usually there is a pattern or reticulation of minute pits. This often takes the form of vertical ridges or ribs associated with more numerous, but less conspicuous, lateral bands. At the top of the egg is a depression in which there is often some ornamentation, being starlike (the rosette) and within which there are a number of minute holes. These are known as micropyles and it is by way of these that the spermatozoa of the male gain entry to the interior of the egg, fusing with the nucleus of the egg-cell and thus fertilizing it. The subsequent growth of the embryo larva can often be seen through the shell and just before hatching the egg darkens considerably.

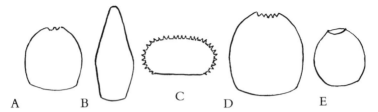

Fig. 1 Outline of generalized egg of the different butterfly families.
A - Hesperidae. B - Pieridae. C - Lycaenidae.
D - Nymphalidae. E - Satyridae.

Usually about 200 or so eggs are laid by each female. They may be laid singly on the food plant, to which they adhere, or they may be laid in batches depending on the species. In some instances, for example the Orange-tip, the egg-laying female examines a food plant and generally lays an egg if no other egg is present. It is bright-orange in colour and easily seen and the larvae of the Orange-tip are noted cannibals as anyone who rears these most attractive butterflies will find out. In a few species, e.g. the Ringlet, there is a tendency for the non-adhesive eggs to be scattered on the ground where the food plants grow abundantly, in this example various species of grass.

LARVA

The newly emerged larva eats the eggshell or some part of it before starting to feed on the food plant. Various explanations for this strange act are to be found in the literature but it appears likely that symbionts, such as micro-fungi, are transferred from the adult to the next generation by being lodged in the pitted surface of the chorion and when eaten are passed to the gut of the young larva. A similar phenomenon is observed in the case of certain wood boring beetles and is probably widespread in insects. The larva of a butterfly is usually known as a caterpillar.

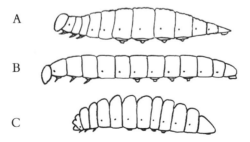

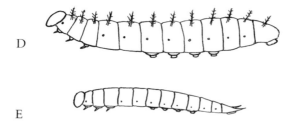

Fig. 2   Outline of generalized larva of the different butterfly families.
A - Hesperiidae. B - Pieridae. C - Lycaenidae.
D - Nymphalidae. E - Satyridae.

Caterpillars are differentiated into two main groups according to shape. Most caterpillars are long and cylindrical (as in the PIERIDAE, NYMPH-ALIDAE and SATYRIDAE) but in the family LYCAENIDAE (comprising the Blues, Hairstreaks and the Small Copper) the caterpillar is slug-like in shape with deep, intersegmental grooves and with a very small head. Usually the head is completely withdrawn into the first thoracic segment.

Basically the caterpillar body consists of a more or less globular head, clearly differentiated from the rest of the body, and thirteen segments, the first three of which form the thorax. Each of the thoracic segments bears a pair of legs (thoracic legs). These are 'true' legs, contrasting with the 'false' or prolegs borne by the abdominal segments. Following the thoracic segments (which correspond with the thorax of the adult butterfly) is the abdomen, consisting of ten segments—although the last two are often difficult to differentiate, so that for general purposes the number of abdominal segments can be said to be nine. Abdominal segments one and two are without legs, but segments three to six each bear a pair of prolegs, and the last segment bears another pair known as the anal claspers, often different in form.

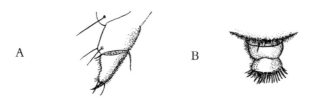

Fig. 3   Legs of larva of butterfly.   A - Thoracic leg. B - Proleg
(Abdominal leg).

19

The thoracic leg consists of three jointed and horny (sclerotised) segments and terminates in a claw. The basal segment is bulbous. The second segment is more or less cylindrical whilst the third is conical. These legs do not function as walking legs but are used to hold steady the leaf on which the larva is feeding. The four pairs of abdominal legs are bulbous structures, each consisting of only two segments, and the apex is blunt with a circle of minute but strong hooks. These give the larva a strong foothold, making the larva difficult to remove by force. Indeed, rupture may occur, so it should never be attempted.

The head of the larva is a horny capsule, more or less spheroidal in shape. If looked at from the front it is flattened with conspicuous rectangular mandibles which act with a sideways motion. Arising from above the mandibles (but apparently extending between them) is the labrum or upper lip at the extremity of which is a long, pointed process—the spinneret from which a silken thread is produced when required, from a gland. At the base of the mandibles on each side, is a small two-segmented antenna which contains the organs of smell and serve the larva in directing it towards its foodplant. The antenna is not nearly as prominent as the same organ present in the adult stage.

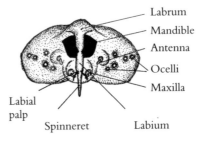

Fig. 4   Oral view of head-capsule of larva of butterfly.

Below the mandibles, one on each side of the spinneret, are the three-segmented maxillae. The terminal segment is claw-like. These develop during the pupal stage to become the long, coiled proboscis of the adult butterfly. On each side of the head are the ocelli, which are organs of sight but seem to be of little use to the larva. (It should be mentioned here that in previous books on butterflies it has been the custom to refer to the eye-like colour patterns on the wings (concentric rings of various colours) as 'ocelli'. This is confusing and they have not been referred to as such in this book.)

Segments of the larva, both thoracic and abdominal, show a similar pattern in the subdivision or subsegments which occur, although the extent of their covering with hairs, bristles or spines (setae) varies enormously.

The larva, as well as the pupa and adult, breathes by means of an intricate network of fine tubules known as tracheae. These open to the exterior through a series of fine openings—the spiracles—one on each side of the first thoracic segment and each abdominal segment except the last. In some cases the spiracles are inconspicuous but in others they are coloured and are easily observed with a x10 hand-lens.

THE PUPA

The old name 'chrysalis' for this the third stage in the life cycle of a butterfly refers to the fact that in a number of species (particularly in the Family NYMPHALIDAE) the external covering is spotted or splashed with a metallic, golden colour. 'Chrysalis' is derived from the Greek word for gold. The word 'pupa' comes from the Latin for doll or puppet. In the pupa there are no external appendages, but the mouth parts, antennae, legs and wings can often be discerned through the horny cuticle. The segmentation of the abdomen can also be seen and these are the only moving parts of the pupa, allowing a limited amount of twisting of the abdomen. In some species this is very much restricted but in a few, e.g. the Dark Green Fritillary, the pupa is able to twirl violently. Generally, however, the pupa is a resting stage between the embryonic 'juvenile' larva and the fully formed, sexually mature adult, and once the change from larva to pupa has occurred, the pupa is unable to move its position. In some species the pupa rests on the ground with or without a loose cocoon of a few leaves drawn together with silken threads. Commonly, however, the abdomen terminates in a short 'stalk' at the tip of which are a number of small hooks. This organ is known as the cremaster. At the point of change from larva to pupa the cremaster emerges from the larval skin (before the skin falls away) and attaches itself to a pad of silk woven by the larva before it takes up its final position.

Fig. 5   Cremaster of pupa.

The method of cremaster attachment described above, where the pupa hangs vertically downwards without any other support, is general in the family NYMPHALIDAE. In the family PIERIDAE, however, in addition to the possession of a cremaster, a silk girdle is spun by the larva over itself with the ends attached to small pads of silk, one on each side, so that the pupa does not hang freely but is fastened at three points.

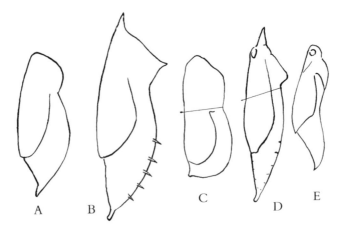

Fig. 6   Outline of generalized pupa of the different butterfly families.
A - Hesperiidae. B - Pieridae. C - Lycaenidae.
D - Nymphalidae. E - Satyridae.

There is a wide variation in the shape of pupae. Some are long and attenuated whilst others are short and wide (dumpy). The spiracles can be seen with a x10 hand-lens. Shortly before the final metamorphosis, the wing colours and the eyes of the adult butterfly can be seen through the pupal cuticle. Then the pupal skin bursts open along the lower edges of the wing cases and also across the thorax and the butterfly pulls itself free. At this point, however, the wings are small and soft and the butterfly crawls a short distance to a convenient position where the wings hang downwards over its back. Fluid is then pumped from the body into the veins of the wings and gradually the wings increase in size to their full extent.

The fluid then hardens and the two surfaces of the wing adhere together and become stiff. The butterfly is not able to fly until this process has been accomplished but the whole metamorphosis takes place within about an hour.

ANATOMY OF THE ADULT BUTTERFLY

The distinction between head, thorax and abdomen in the adult butterfly is very marked, there only being a very narrow 'neck' and 'waist'.

THE HEAD
A large area of the head is taken up by the compound eyes which are globular, each one made up of a number of units or 'facets'. It is not thought, however, that the sense of sight is keen.

Butterflies are generally difficult to approach in bright sunlight and this is probably due more to the acute sense of smell than of sight.

A conspicuous feature of the head is the pair of antennae, commonly referred to as the 'feelers'. These are long, thin, delicate structures made up of a large number of segments and terminated by a 'club'. The shape of the club is variously modified according to species, and in the Dark Green Fritillary it is conspicuously knobbed.

The organs of smell are situated on the antennae, and when the butterfly is sucking nectar from a flower, the antennae will often be seen to be gently waving about. Coiled like a watch-spring at the base of the head and flanked by the hairy but horn-shaped palpi is the proboscis. This organ (which is derived from the auxiliary mouthparts of the larva, not from the mandibles) consists of two tubes, highly segmented and grooved on the inner face.

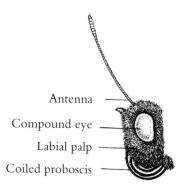

Antenna

Compound eye

Labial palp

Coiled proboscis

Fig. 7   Side view of head of adult butterfly.

The tubes lock together and form a central canal. The extraordinary degree of flexibility is due to the segmentation. The proboscis is used for sucking nectar from flowers and sometimes fluids from decomposing animal bodies or faecal matter. These provide the sole sustenance of the adult butterfly and no solid substances are taken as food in the adult stage. The palpi, already mentioned, cover the front of the head, and further organs of smell are located on them.

THE THORAX

The thorax of a butterfly consists of the first three segments of the body next to the head and corresponds to the same segments in the larval stage and bears the true legs. Indeed, the thorax bears all the organs of locomotion—

a pair of slender legs on each segment and a pair of wings on the second and third segments. This first segment is known as the prothorax and the second and third segments (which are closely joined) the meso- and metathorax respectively. The leg consists of a basal joint, the coxa, which joins the leg to the thorax; a small joint, the trochanter, which connects with the stout femur; the long, slender tibia; and finally the tarsus, which is also long and thin but is divided into five segments, the last of which bears a pair of claws and sometimes special taste organs.

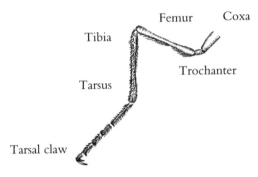

Fig. 8   Leg of adult butterfly.

A butterfly is unable to run but walks fairly slowly, as the chief function of the legs is to hold it on its resting place, the small hooks at the tip of the tarsus being very effective for this purpose.

The families NYMPHALIDAE, SATYRIDAE and DANAIDAE have the first pair of legs reduced so that they cannot be of use in walking, and those of the male are covered with long hairs.

The wings of butterflies are some of the most beautiful structures in the animal kingdom. The diverse colours and often intricate patterns on the large, conspicuous wings of a butterfly constitute one of the most well known phenomena in nature.

Both the upper and the lower surfaces of the wings are covered with minute scales of many different shapes and sizes, but all are fastened to the wing by means of a little 'peg' which fits into a socket in the wing. The scales overlap in the manner of slates on a roof. The colours are derived from two sources. Chemical pigments are probably the principal colour components, but refraction of light (the splitting of white light by means of fine striae, or parallel rows of ridges) is also the source of many lovely colours which change according to the angle of viewing. An example of this derivation of colour is the purple-blue of the Purple Hairstreak butterfly, and the bright blue of the male Common Blue.

Wing scales of a special kind should also be mentioned here. These are the androconia or 'scent-scales', possessed only by the male; they play some part in the stimulation of the female during courtship. They are situated on the forewings, usually forming a conspicuous bar or mark which enables the sex of a butterfly to be determined with accuracy. Most male butterflies carry these scales to a greater or lesser degree.

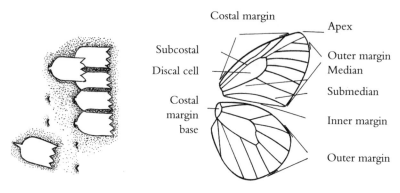

Fig. 9   Part of wing of adult butterfly showing scales highly magnified.

Fig. 10   Wings of butterfly with scales removed showing venation.

The network of veins on the wings has already been mentioned in the expansion of the wings to their full size, and this network (or venation) is remarkably constant for each species; thus the differences in venation are of value in the identification of the species, the genera and families.

The venation is sometimes referred to as neuration and the veins referred to as nerves, but it would seem preferable to use the terms 'venation' and 'veins', as they serve no function except in the pumping of fluid into the wings at the time of metamorphosis and then serve as struts to support the large wing area.

The veins have special names which are shown in Fig. 10. A distinct feature of a butterfly's wing is the presence of an enclosed area extending from the base (where it is narrow) to about halfway along the wing where it is much wider. This is known as the discal cell.

THE ABDOMEN

Occasionally the abdomen consists of ten segments but, when viewed from above, only eight can be seen in the male and seven in the female. The hidden segments are withdrawn into the abdomen and the reproductive organs and their associated processes (the genitalia) are contained within the terminal segments. The spiracles are located on the sides of the prothorax and the abdominal segments (as in the larva) but are inconspicuous owing to the abundant scaling and the covering of fine hairs.

RECORDING

Recording the distribution of butterflies is a worthwhile and rewarding occupation. From the joint efforts of a number of recorders, the first Provisional Distribution Atlas of Butterflies in Ireland was produced by the Irish Biological Records Centre in June 1975. The importance of this atlas is that it gave to recorders information as to which areas have *not* been worked for records. Then, in 1989, Emmet and Heath produced much updated maps for Great Britain and Ireland, with several thousand additional records.

Four criteria are required for a record—firstly, an accurate identification of the butterfly and, secondly, an accurate description of the location. Irish butterflies are not difficult to identify but that is not to say that they can be recognized with precision by someone with only superficial knowledge. The List of Irish Butterflies as shown in the Provisional Atlas mentioned above, or *this book*, should be referred to and the coloured illustrations in the many butterfly books dealing with the British species must also be carefully studied. Access to a good collection of Irish butterflies in a museum is invaluable. But the making of your own private collection is not to be encouraged—in the interests of conservation. A novice should refer all provisional records to an expert before passing them on. Thirdly, the name of the identifier (and/or recorder) must be added. Lastly, the date of the sighting and in both cases, nay in all cases, the writing (or preferably printing) must be legible as all records are of value only if they can be deciphered accurately, being utterly valueless if otherwise.

The criteria given above represent the essential data required for recording the existence of a butterfly (or other animal or plant) in any locality, but the enthusiastic naturalist will want to add other relevant information concerning the habitat. The nature of the ground, direction of flight, existence of other specimens, climatic conditions, food plant species, etc., are all worthy of interest in a notebook or diary when recording.

The traditional method of defining the location in which to record a butterfly (or any other animal or plant), is that of citing the parish or the nearest town or village, and the county. This has often proved to be misleading and usually cumbersome when working out where the location is exactly.

The present method of using the National Grid has a number of advantages in that there is no risk of ambiguity and also it enables mechanical distribution map setting.

What is the Irish National Grid? The Map of Ireland is divided into 100 km squares, or sections, which are identified by letters of the alphabet. On the bottom margin of 1/2" mile maps there is an explanation of the National Grid showing this lettering with reference to the 100 km squares. The large numbers 1, 2 etc on the Atlas maps are the hundreds (1=100, 2=200 etc.) on the National Grid. As an example, the 10 km square most familiar to the author is southwest Co. Cork in which 23 of Ireland's butterflies occur. The location, therefore, is given as VO904, which is the reference to the south-west corner of the square, cutting through Whiddy Island and passing through Bantry and the East.

Recordings should be sent to The Wildlife Service, Spruce House, Leeson Lane, Dublin 2.

The Irish Butterfly and Moth Society is carrying out a national Butterfly Survey and would welcome records of *any* species from any locality in Ireland, and may be contacted at the following address: Butterfly and Moth Records, Country Watch, Castlemaine, Co. Kerry.

ENJOYING BUTTERFLIES

ATTRACTING BUTTERFLIES

One of the most delightful summer and autumn sights is to watch colourful butterflies sipping nectar from garden flowers. They are so engaged in the task that they appear to lose much of their caution, returning again and again to the selfsame blooms. Some plants are well-known as butterfly attractants. Perhaps the *Buddleia davidii*, now commonly called the butterfly bush, is the most widely known. This purple-spiked shrub is a native of China, but grows happily in Ireland and is easily propagated from cuttings. Its annual growth is phenomenal and it should be drastically pruned in late autumn or early spring each year. The species mostly attracted to it are the Small Tortoiseshell, Peacock, Red Admiral, and Painted Lady.

These same species are also attracted to the ice plant, *Sedum spectabile*. This is an easily grown, herbaceous perennial—also from China—and quite hardy. The flower heads are pinkish-purple and the leaves and stems are succulent and blue-green. Flowering stems will remain fresh for many weeks when placed in water and will produce new shoots near the base which can be used for propagation. In cold summers, however, it may flower too late to attract butterflies. The shrubby plants with spikes of small purple flowers (called *Veronica* in the past but now known as *Hebe*) are mostly from New Zealand and attract a number of butterflies.

The well-known herbaceous perennial Michaelmas daisy is very much sought after during autumn and, in addition to Nymphalids, is a certain lure for late Small Coppers.

Plants such as common dock and sorrel should be grown in a 'wild' or untended area of the garden.

A number of indigenous Irish plant species are also sought out for their nectar, and on the subject of the Small Copper butterfly it should be mentioned that the fleabane, *Pulicaria dysenterica*, is especially desired. To walk along a damp ditch bordered by a golden-yellow bank of fleabane on which these little insects sport is one of the countryside's special delights. Perhaps the flowers of the ubiquitous bramble provide the staple source of nectar for the most species, but pride of place should go to the Silver-washed Fritillary which seeks out a freshly opened flower as it floats and glides along a woodland edge or an overgrown hedge wherever the bramble grows. Yet some butterflies are most specific regarding their source of nectar, and a good example is that of the Gatekeeper which will visit bramble but which is readily attracted to two other plants—wood sage, *Teucrium scorodonia*, and marjoram, *Origanum vulgare*. A bed of the latter will usually repay any effort put into it by visits from nectar-seeking butterflies.

BUTTERFLIES AND PLANTS

Butterflies need plants for three different purposes.

Firstly, as food for the larvae, leaves are most generally consumed, but the leaf-buds, flower-buds, flowers and fruit (such as berries) are often eaten also. Some species eat only the buds or the fruit.

Secondly, the nectar of the flowers of many plants is food material for almost all butterflies, and the development of the proboscis for sucking up liquids is directly associated with this. Some species, such as the Red Admiral, feed upon the fluids produced from rotting and fermenting fruit.

Thirdly, certain butterfly species require plants for protection. For example, the Brimstone hibernates through several months of the autumn and winter amongst dense ivy leaves which it closely resembles.

REARING

One of the most popular methods of rearing is to employ a potted-up foodplant. A plastic pot is lightweight and convenient as well as being easy to clean. Use a 13.5 cm or an 18.0 cm diameter pot and place a few pieces of clean slate or broken plant pot at the bottom and fill with a commercial potting compost. There is then no danger of introducing predatory insects, which may be the case when using garden soil. Place the food plant firmly in the compost after checking for aphids and other plant-eating insects. The compost should be really damp. Cover with a clear plastic bag, securing it with a rubber band. The food plant should be potted as long as possible before being put to use.

When an egg-laying adult is available, take off the plastic bag and fit a fine netting (such as butter muslin) using wires or thin sticks to make a 'cage' over the plant—the leg cut from a pair of discarded tights with the foot end cut off is very convenient, as the one end can be closed with a loose knot.

Rearing from the egg stage is by far the most difficult, yet by far, the most rewarding task. That is by contrast with the collecting of the fully grown caterpillars.

Eggs may be obtained from a captured adult female or by diligently searching the foodplants in areas where a particular species is known to occur. The latter method is for the truly observant naturalist, but when one knows exactly what the object looks like, the eye can find the 'needle in the haystack' with comparative ease.

The bright orange eggs of the Orange-tip stand out quite plainly from a distance of several metres when the eye has been trained to find them. Also when the exact location is known the task is simplified—such as in the case of the Brown Hairstreak. In this species the eggs are invariably laid in the fork between two small stems of blackthorn, and so well are they protected that they can be sent through the post without damage!

In considering *which* method of rearing to adopt, almost everything depends on the biology of the species concerned.

Containers for rearing larvae vary in size from a greenhouse to a small, clear plastic box of only a few cubic centimetres capacity. Also they can vary from the makeshift (costing only a few pence) to the very expensive carpenter-made cages of wood and perforated zinc.

For some species, such as the Red Admiral and Silver-washed Fritillary, a cardboard carton is all that is required. A large 'window' is cut from two or three sides (as large as the stability of the carton will allow) and pieces of mosquito netting or curtain netting are cut to size and stuck over the windows with adhesive. Another piece of netting is placed over the open top of the carton, secured by a large rubber band. A potted foodplant, or a portion of it in water, must be placed in the carton. There are, of course, many variants of this including the use of large, perspex jars, but different difficulties may occur according to the biology of the species to be reared. For example, the Dingy Skipper is adept at escaping through the smallest hole, and if perspex jars are used they must never be placed in full sun.

An important method of rearing larvae is known as 'sleeving'. In this a sleeve of netting is placed over a branch of the naturally growing foodplant. However, this is only really practical in the case of shrubs and trees, so that only a few species are involved (the Hairstreaks, Brimstone and Holly blue). It has to be borne in mind that a number of hymenopterous parasites, because of their minute size, can also enter the sleeve. In addition, overcrowding must be avoided or cannibalism may occur. The advantage of sleeving, however, is that the larvae feed under more or less natural conditions whilst at the same time being protected from birds and prevented from wandering.

Perhaps the greatest difficulty in rearing butterflies arises with those spending a long time (many months) in the egg stage or as tiny larvae. Dr Tolman has helped tremendously by explaining his 'culture' method (my term) in respect of the Brown Hairstreak. In this species, as already mentioned, the winter is spent in the egg stage in the fork between two small stems. As in all cases of small creatures kept in captivity for some months, the greatest problem is to maintain such conditions of temperature and humidity that the animal will neither desiccate nor support fungal growth. This entails an almost daily examination. When the food plant first shows activity it must be introduced to the container holding the eggs or egg, and in the case of the Brown Hairstreak, this is when the flower buds of blackthorn first begin to swell to show the white of the enclosed petals. Every day thereafter the container must be examined and the blackthorn bud removed and a fresh one substituted. Not only in this instance, but in almost all others, the removal of the stale plant is a most important factor in successful butterfly rearing.

One excellent result which attends the rearing of butterfly species, especially when commencing with a large number of eggs, is that the natural mortality rate is greatly reduced. The incidence of parasitism and predation can be decreased by careful management, and the resulting adult butterflies can be released—a very satisfying consequence. But make sure that abundant food plants of the appropriate species are available locally. Rare species should not be released outside their natural range.

FOOD PLANTS

GARDEN NASTURTIUM, *Tropaeolum majus*

This South American annual of the family TROPAEOLACEAE is a common food plant of both the Large and Small White butterflies. It is one of the most popular garden annuals used for bedding and edging in its 'dwarf' forms, or for covering banks and trellis in its climbing and trailing varieties. The leaves are circular with a wavy edge and the stems have a succulent or waxy appearance. The flower is about 50 mm across and its petals are bright yellow or orange, with the prolonged sepals creating a long spur. When the plant is crushed a pungent odour is released. Altogether there are about ninety species in the genus, including canary creeper, *Tropaeolum peregrinum*.

STINGING NETTLE, *Urtica dioica*

This obnoxious weed is one of the most important plants for the conservation of Ireland's butterflies. It is the sole food plant for the larvae of three of our showy and abundant species of the NYMPHALIDAE—the Small Tortoiseshell, the Peacock, and the immigrant Red Admiral. Very occasionally the larvae of the immigrant Painted Lady also feed on it.

The stinging nettle is found throughout Ireland, being abundant wherever the nitrogen content of the soil is more than average, such as where human habitation (past or present) occurs, especially near farms, road verges and waste places. The conservationist should allow a patch to grow in his or her garden. An important point is that the plant should be cut back in July so that new growth is available for the second broods of the Small Tortoiseshells, as well as for the immigrant Red Admiral.

MEADOW VETCHLING, *Lathyrus pratensis*

Several different species of the LEGUMINOSAE have been noted as larval foodplants of the Wood White. Generally the following species are reported— bird's-foot trefoil, *Lotus corniculatus*, and common vetch, *Vicia cracca*. However, eggs were found by the author on meadow vetchling in Co. Waterford near a roadside at Lismore. It is an abundant plant thereabouts and doubtless it is the general food plant in that locality. Meadow vetchling is a straggling herbaceous plant easy to identify. The 4–10 cm flowers are yellow and the stem is long and thin. The leaf consists of a pair of narrow pointed leaflets and a terminal tendril. Stipules are present which are similar to the leaflets, but have pointed auricles. It is common in hedges and ditches, occurring also in damp meadows.

WATERCRESS, *Nasturtium officinale*

This member of the CRUCIFERAE is also known a *Rorippa nasturtium-aquaticum* and, together with the closely related species *N.microphyllum*, is found in streams and ditches throughout the country. Larvae of the Green-veined White butterfly commonly feed upon it.

The flowering shoot illustrated (Fig. 18E), was 120 mm in length when collected and had nine eggs of this species on the underside of the leaves. They are laid singly, although two or more may be found on the same leaflet.

BUCKTHORN, *Rhamnus catharticus* and ALDER BUCKTHORN, *Rhamnus Frangula*

Two species of the family RHAMNACEAE (both tree or shrubs) occur in Ireland. Both are the only hosts to the larvae of the Brimstone butterfly, so that the distribution of this butterfly is determined by the distribution of these two shrubs. However, there are records of the Brimstone being seen far away from the locality of its food plants. The two species are easily differentiated. Alder buckthorn *R. frangula,* is devoid of spines and has un-toothed leaves somewhat like those of the alder. The leaves are always alternate and all the flower parts are in fives. This species is said to be very rare, and only found in rocky and boggy situations. I found it on Ross Island at Killarney, where the Brimstone is very rare.

The second species, buckthorn, *Rhamnus catharticus,* is a spiny shrub with alternate, toothed leaves about 37 mm in length and with its flower parts in fours. It is occasionally found in rocky places and on rocky shores in the west and centre of the country, but elsewhere is rare. Both species are quite easily cultivated, so the avid conservationist should grow these two shrubs.

BLACKTHORN/SLOE, *Prunus spinosa*
This is a common shrub found widely in Ireland but, is the food plant of one of the country's rarest butterflies—the Brown Hairstreak. Blackthorn is easy to identify. The twigs are black and the branches end in stout spines; the leaves are finely toothed and not longer than 35 mm. The white flowers are from 10–15 mm across and appear before the leaves from March to May. The Brown Hairstreak larvae will also feed on the flower buds and young shoots of cultivated plum when in captivity, so would most probably also feed on the bullace (wild plum), *Prunus domestica,* which is less spiny than blackthorn, with brown stems rather than black, and flowers appearing with the leaves.

WHITE BEAKED SEDGE, *Rhynchospora alba*
Information on the food plants of the Large Heath butterfly is very sparse and somewhat misleading. The eggs appear to be laid mainly on the white beaked-sedge, placed in the CYPERACEAE and therefore a *sedge* (not a *grass* as given by Howarth, 1973).

This plant is about 15 cm in height, light green and spiky with whitish inflorescence which appear star-like when viewed from above. The very narrow leaves are ribbed. Webb (1977) states that it occurs in lowland bogs, is common in the west and midlands, but is rather rare in the south and east of the country. Frohawk (1924) found that the Large Heath larvae would feed on several grass species, especially *Poa annua* and *Festuca glauca,* when in captivity.

HONESTY and SWEET ROCKET
Everyone interested in butterflies must surely grow a patch of honesty, *Lunaria annua,* and sweet rocket, *Hesperis matronalis,* in the garden—unfashionable and old-fashioned as many will look upon them. When once the seeds of honesty have been sown, it will generally re-seed itself if the attractive fruits with their silvery septa are left on the plant and not used as part of dried flower arrangements. It is a biennial with reddish-purple flowers. Sweet rocket is another old-time garden plant upon which the Orange-tip larvae will feed. The usual

food plant, lady's smock, is indicative of damp and boggy conditions—not often tolerated in suburban gardens.

PLANTS FOR SCARCE IMMIGRANTS

It might seem a very long chance to cater for scarce immigrant butterflies in one's garden, but surely that extra effort and care is worthwhile.

Even though some species have been recorded but a few times, it must be borne in mind that the number of recorders being in the right place at the right time would be very small. Obviously many butterflies visit the Irish shores far more often than official records show. What can we do about this?

We should set about planting the larval food plants of these immigrants in both public and private gardens so that eggs can be laid by fertilized females which have survived the passage over the sea. This is a fairly easy task with regard to the Queen of Spain Fritillary whose larvae will feed on the cultivated pansy and beds or borders holding this variety could easily be arranged on an annual basis. The foodplants of other immigrants are found under the respective species account in the main body of the text.

CONSERVATION

LAWNS

Perhaps one of the most important types of site of potential value in butterfly conservation is the lawn. Commonly consisting of a few short-growing grass species, it is cut at frequent intervals during the summer. The mower with which this operation is carried out, has been developed into a precision instrument capable of cutting the grass to a length (or shortness) of 10mm. This virtually eliminates all but a few species of grass. In addition, the gardener takes out all plants in competition with the fine grasses mechanically, or by the use of selective herbicides. The worms are killed also, because of the so-called unsightly nature of their casts. Yet if lawns were kept at about 50mm length, a wealth of plant species would find lodgement and flourish.

It is conceded by the author that a new concept of what a lawn should be would have to be considered, especially by the more traditional of our gardeners.

When the more 'butterfly-desirable' plant species make their appearance, there is probably a more sophisticated type of lawn management required than for the formal lawn.

Lawns consisting of species other than grasses are well known, and consist of but one plant species; the practical butterfly conservationist should not object to this if such plants are of value to butterflies.

Bird's foot trefoil, *Lotus corniculatus*, often makes its appearance in a lawn which is just kept trimmed and not shaven. It usually thrives in such a situation and the Common Blue will sometimes cause delight by finding it. The Dingy Skipper's larvae also feed on it, so it is a plant always to be encouraged.

The larvae of satyrids feed on a number of grass species, but they usually prefer rather coarser ones such as cock's-foot, which does not do well if trimmed. So the seeds of this species should be collected and sown in a 'wild area' along a hedge or bank.

SHELTER

There is another way in which we can contribute towards conserving butterflies. That is by providing shelter for those species which pass the winter in hibernation in the adult stage. Virtually only three species are involved: the Peacock, Small Tortoiseshell, and Brimstone. Although one would expect our immigrants, the Red Admiral and the Painted Lady, to be able to survive a fairly mild winter, they fail to do so. There seems to be some climatic element which prevents this. There have been no reliable records of the Red Admiral passing the winter with us, and none at all for the Painted Lady.

But the Small Tortoiseshell, and to a lesser extent the Peacock, is influenced very much by humans in its chances of survival until the following spring. Early July finds the Small Tortoiseshells emerged and, briefly, for a few days, sipping nectar from thistles, *Buddleia*, knapweeds and other flowers attractive to them; but they are soon searching for their hibernation sites. These are commonly in sheds and roof voids, but they are often tempted to hang in curtain folds and other nooks and crannies in living rooms and bedrooms. This is usually satisfactory, but occasionally it is not.

It sometimes happens that, in mid-winter, the living-room in which the Small Tortoiseshell is hibernating becomes very warm and humid, due to the number of people using the room. The butterfly then becomes active, commencing to flutter around, but to put it outside on a chilly night is condemning it to certain death. Butterflies appear to fare better in bedrooms, as these do not usually get anywhere near as hot as living rooms and kitchens. Even so, during the first warm days of Spring, activity must be watched for as now they must be allowed to escape. The Small Tortoiseshell hibernates (or rather aestivates) in July when windows are left open, but in late March to early April, they may be kept shut, at least for much of the time. This is where the dusty, old garden shed can be of such importance! In a state of wild nature, before Man intruded, the Small Tortoiseshell and the Peacock hibernated in hollow trees and caves. The old garden shed is now substituted for both. If old rough planks are available, lean them slantwise against the backwall so that a butterfly resting on the underside does not present its silhouette to a potential predator. The shed should be filled with drab-coloured garden impedimenta, such as stacks of old seed boxes, twine, canes, etc. It is probably not necessary to enumerate in detail—doubtless someone will come up with the ideal *nymphalid hibernaculum*, and good luck to them!

In forestry areas, piles of closely stacked logs are known to be favoured by Peacocks for hibernation.

Another butterfly which can be helped by the provision of shelter during hibernation is the Brimstone. This species habitually spends the winter amongst the dense foliage of ivy or sometimes holly. Indeed, the shape and colour of the closed wings resemble dead and yellowing ivy leaves, even to the extent of bearing a few mould-like spots! There are those who have the mistaken idea that ivy is a parasite on trees, which it is not. We should do all we can to keep our ivy—not only does it shelter the Brimstone but the flower buds are the larval food of the second brood of Holly Blues. It is, therefore, an important plant for two of our butterflies, as well as being the larval food plant of several moths, including the large, yellow Swallowtail moth.

Additionally, the opening flowers in autumn provide nectar for a host of insects—even into late autumn. The Red Admiral commonly feeds on ivy nectar until the frosty nights occur. Ivy berries provide winter feed for a number of bird species, so instead of cutting down our ivy, we should aim to cultivate it in gardens and parks, not only allowing it to cover brick walls, but also to be planted here and there so that it can scramble up a tree, especially one that is perhaps past its prime.

RESIDENT SPECIES

FAMILY HESPERIIDAE

The sole Irish member of the world-wide family HESPERIIDAE is the Dingy Skipper. This family consists of several thousand species. Typical of the hesperiid butterflies are the stout body, large head and the widely spaced substantial antennae which are angled at the tip. The apex of the forewing is rather pointed and the wings are held around the body when resting—much in the fashion of moths. The members of the family have the common name of Skippers, derived from their short darting flight or "skipping".

Fig. 11 Family Hesperiidae. Dingy Skipper, *Erynnis tages*. Note recurved antennae, large head and thickset body. An extreme form of subspecies *baynesi* from the Burren.

DINGY SKIPPER

Erynnis tages subspecies *tages* (Linnaeus, 1758)

The Dingy Skipper inhabits dry sunny banks, rough hillsides, and wasteland where the larval foodplant, bird's foot trefoil, *Lotus corniculatus*, occurs. Ssp. *Baynesi* is sometimes especially abundant in limestone areas; thus it is not widespread throughout Ireland, being restricted to the Burren in Clare and a number of localities eastwards to the coast at Co. Dublin. It occurs in Cos. Wexford, Waterford, Sligo, Mayo, Donegal and Fermanagh.

In the evening and in dull weather it can be easily observed resting on the tips of tall grasses, sometimes in association with the Common Blue. Its flight, or 'skipping', is remarkably fast and often defeats the eye in the attempt to follow it.

ADULT (Fig. 12D, Plate I A)
This small, rather sombre-coloured butterfly, measures about 29mm across the outstretched wings. The head and body are thick and sturdy, and in the case of the male, there is a fold along the base of the costal margin of the forewings. The general ground colour is 'fuscous-brown' and in the fore-

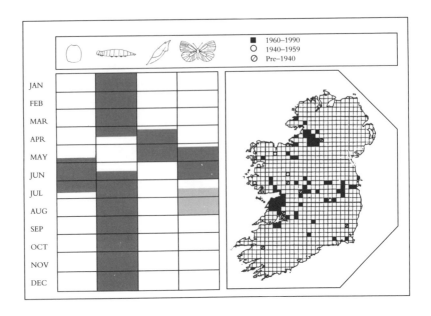

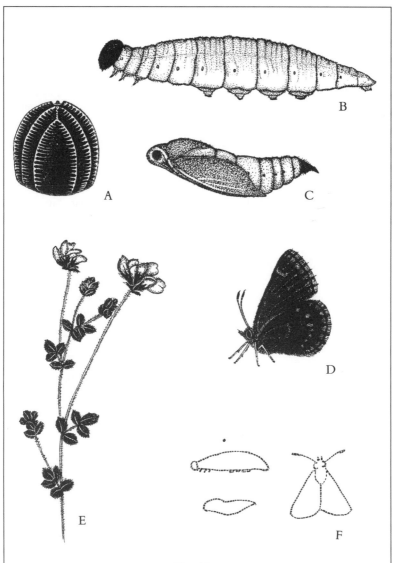

Fig. 12

Dingy Skipper: A - Egg (ht. 0.5mm, dia. 0.5mm); B - Larva
(L 17.5mm); C - Pupa (L 14mm); D - Adult, side-view (wing-
span 29mm); E - Food plant: Bird's foot trefoil, *Lotus corniculatus*.
F – Life Size.

wings there are ill-defined, transverse, grey bands bordered with blackish blotches, the outer row of the latter edged with dark brown, bordered on the inside with white spots.

In the hindwings there is a row of pale spots near the centre and the fringes are fairly conspicuous, grey and flecked. The ground colour of the underside is paler—'golden-brown'. The spotting of the upper surface is repeated. The female lacks the costal fold and the undersides of the wings are darker, with the pattern marks rather more conspicuous. There is much variation in the distinctness of the banding and spotting, and in the subspecies *baynesi* the light markings are very pale grey—often nearly white—whereas the ground colour is contrasted by being much darker. This subspecies occurs only in the Burren, Co Clare, south Galway, and parts of west Limerick.

This butterfly is single-brooded and flies in May and June, but the possibility of a second brood in August should not be overlooked.

EGG (Fig. 12A)
The egg is spherical in shape with a flattened base, and the micropyle situated in the depression at the apex. It is 0.5 mm in height and about the same in width. About 13 conspicuous white, fluted ridges originate near the micropyle and run down the side. About 6 ridges run to the base directly whilst the remainder bifurcate shortly after passing over the crown—thus perhaps 20 ridges reach the base. Between the ridges, the surfaces are concave with many very fine, transverse ribs.

At first the egg is a pale primrose-yellow, but this gradually deepens to a rich 'apricot-orange' with light yellow ridges.

At about the seventh day the embryo larva may be seen through the shell, appearing greenish-brown with a dark grey head. It hatches after 10 to 12 days.

Eggs are laid singly on the tips of the leaflets of bird's foot trefoil, *Lotus corniculatus*, and *Lotus villosus*.

LARVA (Fig. 12B)
On hatching the larva spins a few *Lotus* leaves together, forming a shelter in which it feeds. New 'shelters' are constructed as the previous shelter is devoured until the larva is fully fed (about the beginning of August), when it measures about 17.5 mm in length.

The body tapers both in front and behind, but more so at the front. The first thoracic segment is very small, making the purplish-black and rust-mottled head appear large in proportion. The body segments are conspicuously subdivided—each into about five with the anterior (nearest the front) one of each segment being the largest.

The ground colour is apple-green tinged with light brownish-yellow which is darkest dorsally. There is a whitish line on each side and the spiracles are dark brown. The body surface is liberally covered with whitish bristles, each arising from a black white-encircled base, giving the larva a whitish sheen.

When fully fed, the larva hibernates in a reinforced shelter until about the following April, or early-May, when it pupates within this compact strong cocoon.

The total duration of the larval stage is 10–11 months.

PUPA (Fig. 12C)

The slender pupa is about 14 mm in length and about 3.8 mm at the widest point. The head is rounded and the eyes are conspicuous. The head, thorax, and wing-cases are dark green, whilst the abdomen is rusty-red with a greenish tinge.

The thoracic spiracle is adjacent to a black, ear-like tuft consisting of black bristles. The pupa is firmly attached to the cocoon by cremastral hooks.

The pupal stage lasts 32 to 36 days.

FAMILY PIERIDAE

The family PIERIDAE contains six of Ireland's resident butterfly species, popularly known as the 'Whites' and 'Yellows'. All are more or less marked with black, except one, the Brimstone. All six legs are functional and used for walking in contrast with the families NYMPHALIDAE and SATYRIDAE, in which only four of the legs are used for walking. The tall, ribbed eggs are skittle-shaped or bottle-shaped, and the caterpillars are slender with a velvet-like surface. Spines are absent. The pupae are girdled with a silken thread and attached to the substrate by a cremaster, hooked onto a silken pad. A cocoon is absent. The family is world-wide in distribution. Three subfamilies are represented in Ireland; the DISMORPHIINAE, COLIADINAE and PIERINAE.

Fig. 13 Family Pieridae. Green-veined White, *Pieris napi* Subspecies *brittanica*. Species in this family are predominantly white or yellow.

WOOD WHITE

Leptidea sinapis subspecies *juvernica* (Williams)

The Wood White is usually found along the borders of woodland paths and in rough, uncultivated ground. In some areas, however, it flourishes far from woodland—in the Burren, Co. Clare, it is found on the rough ground near the coast, and it is frequently abundant along railway cuttings elsewhere. The larval food plants all belong to the family LEGUMINOSAE and include bird's foot trefoil, *Lotus corniculatus,* and common vetch, *Vicia cracca.* There is generally one brood annually, although in some years two may occur. The winter is passed in the pupal stage and the adult is on the wing from early May to late June.

The Wood White is widespread throughout Ireland. It is particularly common in the east, but is not so well-recorded in the west (except for Co. Clare) and the north. In recent years there has been a marked increase in its distribution, (Heal, 1965; Lavery, 1992).

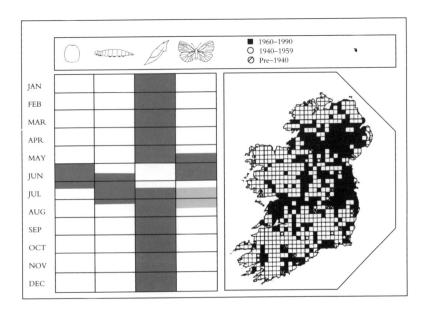

■ 1960–1990
O 1940–1959
⊘ Pre–1940

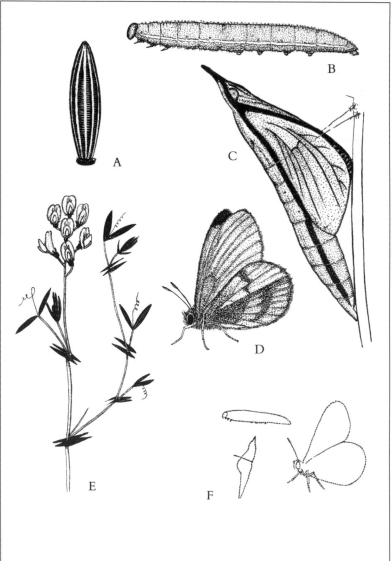

Fig. 14

Wood White: A - Egg (ht. 1.3mm); B - Larva (L 19mm):
C - Pupa (L 16mm); D - Adult, side-view (wing-span 42mm);
E - Food plant: Yellow meadow vetchling, *Lathyrus pratensis*.
F – Life size.

PIERIDAE

ADULT (Fig. 14D, Plate I D)
The outstretched wings generally measure 42 mm in both sexes. The ground colour of this delicate-looking butterfly is milky white. When at rest the wings are held vertically over the body.

In the male, the forewings are greyish at the base of the front (costal) margins and there is a dark-grey streak at the base of the hind margins. At the apex is a more or less rectangular grey or blackish blotch, and below it the tips of the veins are also greyish. Except for two greyish streaks at the base, the hindwings are uniformly white, although the veins (which are darkly marked on the underside) show through. On the underside of the forewings the apical area is yellowish, with the veins greenish due to grey scaling, and the base of the forewings is grey, outlining the discal cell. The hindwings are greenish-yellow with the veins grey and more heavily marked and blotched across the wings.

The female has the front margin of the forewings more rounded than the male, which makes the wings broader, and the markings are less concentrated with the apical blotch reduced. This generally leaves the tip white with the veins marked with grey.

EGG (Fig. 14A)
This is long and spindle-shaped and about 1.3 mm in height, pointed at the apex and standing on a small pedestal by which it is glued to the underside of the leaf of various leguminous herbs. There are about 11 longitudinal ridges and many minute transverse ribs. In colour it is pale lemon-yellow and shiny, but becomes brownish shortly before the young larva emerges. The length of this stage lasts from 7 to 11 days.

LARVA (Fig. 14B)
Soon after the fourth moult the larva is full-grown and about 19 mm in length. It is bright green and cylindrical in form, exceedingly slender, and gradually narrowing towards the hinder end. The transverse, flap-like last segment overhangs the anal segment. It is seldom seen in any other position but in a straight line, and doubtless derives most benefit from this as it is most difficult to observe when stretched out along the stem or stalk of its usual food plants. Each segment is sub-divided into 6 transverse rings. Running the whole length of the body is a dark-green stripe, and there is a well-defined yellow stripe along the sides; small, white spiracles are situated along the upper surface. Immediately above the yellow stripe the green ground colour is darker, but lightens towards the back. The head is green.

A characteristic feature of the larva is the presence of minute processes occurring in 6 longitudinal rows which, in the first instar larva, are Y-shaped. In addition, other spines are present, a pair of which on the back of each segment bear a globule of fluid at their tips. The larval stage lasts about 30 days.

PUPA (Fig. 14C)

The fully fed larva spins a silken patch for its anal claspers and a girdle and then assumes a hook-like position before pupating. The pupa is about 16 mm in length, but of those reared by the author, one was 15.5 mm and another was 17.5 mm. In form it is slender with a sharply pointed beak which is slightly upturned. The general ground colour is light green to pale yellow, at first translucent. Running from the beak to the cremaster is a conspicuous lilac-coloured, practically straight line, which borders the margin of the wing before traversing the middle line of the abdomen in which the spiracles are situated. The wing cases form a prominent triangular region projecting downwards from the abdomen, but note that the pupa usually hangs outwards at an angle, with the ventral surface uppermost. The lilac stripe divides behind the head and traverses the outer margin of the wing cases. The veins of the wings are also finely marked with the lilac colour, as are the antennae and parts of the head between the wing cases. There is a mid-dorsal, thin longitudinal, dark green line. The intensity of colouration, however, varies much between different specimens.

Two or three days before emergence the colour darkens, and the adult colouration is plainly visible through the delicate parchment-like pupal cuticle. The pupal stage lasts about 10 months.

BRIMSTONE

Gonepteryx rhamni subspecies *gravesi* Huggins, 1956

This species is locally common wherever its foodplants occur. Whereas the other Irish members of the PIERIDAE pass the winter as pupae, the Brimstone hibernates as an adult.

ADULT (Fig. 15D, Plate I B,C)
The Irish race is distinctive and is given subspecific rank as ssp. *gravesi*. One of the first butterflies to be seen in spring is the brilliant yellow male Brimstone. It is tempted out of hibernation by the first sunny warm day of the year, having spent the winter amongst dense ivy growing on a wall or a tree. Indeed, the shape and colouration of the Brimstone's wings closely resemble the shape and colour of a dying ivy leaf, even to the extent of mould stains!

The distance across the expanded wings varies from about 60 mm–75 mm and both hind and fore wings are sharply angled with the venation prominent. The colour of the upper side of the male is lemon-yellow, but the hindwings show a slight tinge of greenish. An orange spot is placed near the tip of the

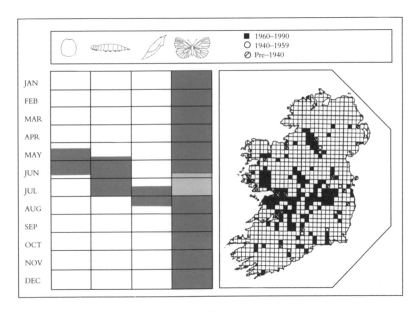

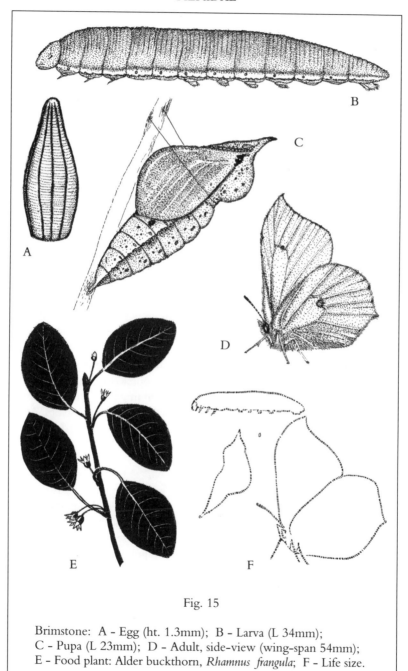

Fig. 15

Brimstone: A - Egg (ht. 1.3mm); B - Larva (L 34mm);
C - Pupa (L 23mm); D - Adult, side-view (wing-span 54mm);
E - Food plant: Alder buckthorn, *Rhamnus frangula*; F - Life size.

discoidal cell in both the fore- and hindwings, those spots on the latter being the larger. Along the margins there is a series of small chocolate-brown spots, one at the termination of each vein. The thorax and abdomen are black above (yellowish underneath) with black extending into a small patch at the base of each wing. The thorax and upper abdomen are covered with long white hairs. The antennae are comparatively short and pinkish in colour. The underside of the wings is much paler and duller, tinged with greenish. The orange spots on the upper surface are seen as brown on the underside. The upper surface of the wings of the male is paler and more muted yellow than the English form, and the hindwings are not nearly so greenish.

The female is greenish yellow with the forewings bordered with a more yellowish tinge, whilst the hindwings are suffused with the same colour. Specimens of the British race (ssp. *rhamni* (L)) have been introduced into Tipperary, but it is unknown if they survived long enough to breed with local ssp. *gravesi*.

EGG (Fig. 15A)

The eggs are laid singly on the underside of a leaf (generally on the mid-rib). There are two species of food plant, buckthorn, *Rhamnus catharticus*, and Alder buckthorn, *Rhamnus frangula*. Eggs are laid during the second half of May and the first half of June (but sometimes later), resulting in larvae of different sizes occurring on the same food plant. The egg is tall and bottle-shaped, being about 1.3 mm in height and widest at the middle, decreasing to the flat base which is firmly adhered to the leaf. Towards the rounded apex the egg narrows considerably. Generally there are ten ridges running longitudinally, almost reaching the apex, and there are about forty-five minute transverse ribs. At first the colour is pale, bluish-green but this gradually becomes a deep yellow darkening to grey shortly before hatching.

The egg stage lasts about 10 days.

LARVA (Fig. 15B)

The fully grown larva is generally from 32–35 mm in length and is long, thin and uniformly cylindrical, except for the first thoracic segment which is small and increases in size from the head to the second segment. The last three segments decrease in size and the anal segment is pointed. All the segments are transversely grooved. The upper surface is glaucus-green, darker on the back and gradually becoming tinged with bluish towards the sides before joining the white spiracular stripe which gives it a somewhat 'frosty' appearance. The spiracles are whitish with the apertures tinged with yellow. The under surface is clear yellowish-green, but is generally hidden by the laterally prolonged spiracular stripe. The whole larva has a velvety appearance which is brought about by the dense covering of minute black pedestal-shaped tubercles, each of which has an even smaller spike. The larva usually rests along the mid-rib of a leaf with the claspers at the base, returning to this position after eating portions of the apical leaf area. If disturbed, even to the slightest degree, the larva raises its front end. The length of the larval period is about one month.

PUPA (Fig. 15C)

This is about 22-24 mm in length and about 9.5 mm in width at the widest part. It is quite unlike any other butterfly pupa. The front of the head bears a strong, upwards-curving beak which is dark at the tip, and the thoracic pronota are bulbous. The wing cases are large and project downwards to form a strong rounded keel. The abdomen terminates in a bifid cremaster which is fixed to a silken pad. The body is encircled by a fine silken thread which holds the pupa away from the twig or leaf to which it is fastened.

The general colour of the pupa is bright green, but there is a darker green, narrow mid-dorsal line; a dark line runs from the base of the antennae along the margin of the wing case and is continued along the abdomen, slightly above the yellow spiracles to the cremaster. There is a purplish-brown, star-shaped blotch at the base of the wing cases and a sprinkling of drab-coloured spots on the body, with a mottling on the wing cases.

There is another, but smaller, purplish-brown spot on the underside of the abdomen near the outer margin of the wing case. Shortly before emergence a male pupa will turn a brilliant yellow, and the vermilion marginal marks and red antennae of the adult can be clearly seen.

The pupal stage lasts about fourteen days.

LARGE WHITE

Pieris brassicae (Linnaeus, 1758)

This is usually a plentiful butterfly with the numbers sometimes being considerably increased by immigration. After years of exceptional abundance, however, the population number is known to crash. It is sometimes injurious to *Brassica* crops.

Double-brooded, the adults are seen on the wing from April to June and then again from July to September.

Winter is passed in the pupal stage.

ADULT (Fig. 16D, Plate I E,F)
The male of this species measures 63.5 mm across the outstretched wings and the larger female sometimes is as much as 76.2 mm. On the upper surface the ground colour is milky-white.

In the male the forewings are tipped with black and are greyish at the apex in the spring brood, while in the summer brood this greyish area is almost

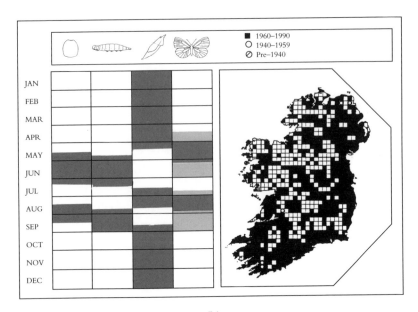

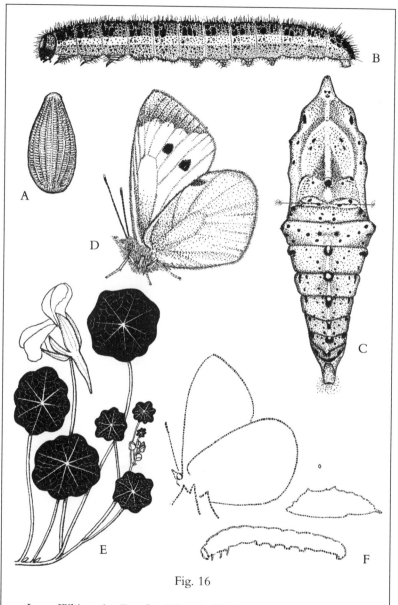

Fig. 16

Large White; A - Egg (ht. 1.2mm); B - Larva (L 41mm):
C - Pupa (L 23mm); D - Adult, side-view (wing-span male
63.5mm, female 76.2mm); E - Food plant: Nasturtium, *Tropaeolum*;
F - Life size.

absent. The base of all wings is dark grey in the spring brood, but very much more lightly marked in the summer brood. The hindwings bear a single, grey mark on the front margin. On the underside of the forewing it is yellow dusted with grey, and there are two black spots towards the centre. The hindwing is yellow with the veins grey, especially near the base of the wing. In the summer brood there is far less grey.

The female is easily distinguished from the male by the presence of two black spots and a black, transverse bar on the hind margin of the forewings and, in addition, the hindwings are usually more yellowish.

EGG (Fig. 16A)
This is erect and skittle-shaped and is about 1.20 mm in height. The basal part is elliptical, but the apex is elongated. It is widest just below the middle. About 18 longitudinal ridges run from near the granulated, rounded apex to the flattened base. Between the ridges the surface is concave and there are about 40 minute, lateral ribs, giving the appearance of fine basketware. At first the colour is creamy yellow, but as they are laid in batches, the colour appears a deeper yellow. The summit becomes whitish until a day or so before hatching when the dark head of the embryo may be seen through the shell. The egg stage lasts from about four and a half days to seventeen days according to the temperature, but is normally about seven days.

LARVA (Fig. 16B)
The larva reaches a length of about 41 mm after four moults and is roughly cylindrical in shape, tapering only slightly at each end. The general background colour is greyish-green, but the whole body is covered with black, irregular, rounded blotches, although many are minute. Located on the blotches are small, black-pointed tubercles from which a white or black curved hair arises. On the anal segment is a glistening black disc, giving the impression that it is the head. The head, however, is black with a light-grey area on each side, and the clypeus is pale yellow. There are three, longitudinal stripes of yellow, one down the middle of the back and one on each side along the line of spiracles. The underside of the larva is light, greenish-brown and the spiracles are flesh-coloured, margined with dark brown, but only distinguishable with difficulty.

During the early stages, the young larva spins silk over the surface of the leaf and feeds and rests together with other larvae as a small batch, but they do not spin silk after the fourth moult, although they are still gregarious. They make no attempt to hide, feeding openly in daylight, and are presumed to be distasteful to birds and other predators.

PUPA (Fig. 16C)

All nine pupa reared by the author were 23 mm in length and 6.5 mm in width. They were all bright apple-green with a dull sheen and many black spots, and the mid-dorsal line is yellow. It was firmly held by the cremaster from a patch of silk and was encircled by a silken girdle around the middle. The ends of the girdle were woven out from small, silk patches fixed to the substrate. All the pupa were fixed vertically as there was little in the way of horizontal support in the container in which they pupated.

SMALL WHITE

Pieris rapae (Linnaeus, 1758)

As with the preceding species, the Small White is a widely distributed and abundant butterfly. In some years, large numbers of immigrants have been noted. There are two and sometimes three broods annually.

The adult butterfly is on the wing during April, May and again in June and July, and the winter is passed in the pupal stage. The larvae feed on numerous species of the family CRUCIFERAE (the Cabbage family) as well as on the garden nasturtium, *Tropaeolum majus*, and the garden mignonette, *Reseda odorata*. The larvae are often injurious to garden-grown cabbages.

ADULT (Fig. 17D, Plate I G)
This species measures about 50 mm across the wings in both sexes, but there is much variation in size. The ground colour is milky-white but varies to deep cream.

The male of the spring brood has the apex of the forewing faintly grey with one very pale spot towards the centre of the wing and a darker, greyish spot on the front margin of the hindwing. On the underside, the apex of the forewing is

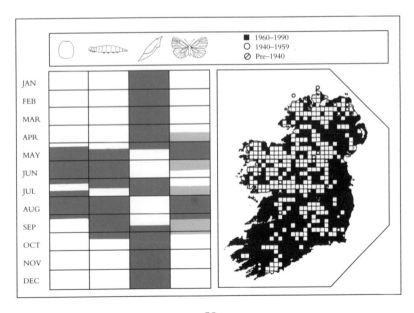

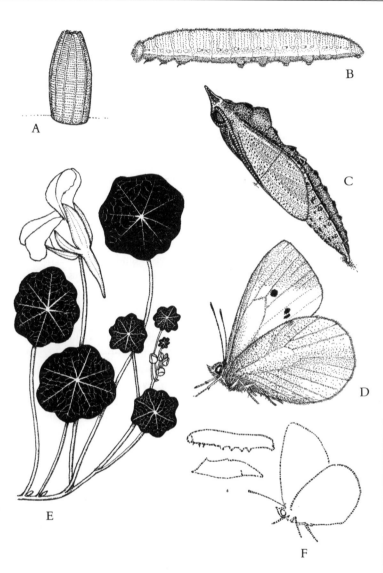

Fig. 17

Small White: A - Egg (ht. mm); B - Larva (L 25mm); C - Pupa
(L 19mm); D - Adult, side-view (wing-span 50mm);
E - Food plants: Nasturtium, *Tropaeolum majus*; F - Life size.

yellow and there is a dark grey spot towards the centre. The hindwing is yellow with the base greyish and the veins lightly dusted with grey.

The female has two greyish-black spots and a bar on the forewing with a more pronounced spot on the front margin of the hindwing. The ground colour is creamier—often quite yellow with the bases of the wings duskier. In the summer brood the marking is much more pronounced; almost black rather than grey—especially the apex of the forewing and the central spot in the middle of the male forewing. In the female the ground colour is much yellower than in the spring brood.

EGG (Fig. 17A)

This is rounded, conical, and elongate in shape and stands on a flat base. It is about 1 mm in height. It is widest a little above the middle and there are about 12 longitudinal ridges. Eight of the latter originate at the apex and the remaining four, in two pairs, a little below. Fine, transverse ribbing is present—about 35 ribs in all. When freshly laid the egg is pale yellowish-green (almost white) but within a few days it becomes more yellowish. Under optimum conditions the egg stage lasts as little as 72 hours, but in other circumstances it may take a week before hatching.

LARVA (Fig. 17B)

This predominantly pale green caterpillar reaches a length of about 25 mm after moulting four times, remaining only about twenty days in this stage. It consumes its cast skin after each moult. Being nearly uniformly cylindrical in shape, only the first and last segments are somewhat smaller.

The upper surface of the body is mid-green, whilst the lower is whitish green. A light greenish-yellow, narrow line extends along the median dorsal surface from the head to the eleventh and sometimes the twelfth segment. The whole body is covered with small, black tubercles, some of which are very small. Each bears a hair and those of the dorsal surface are somewhat knobbed. The flesh-coloured spiracles are margined with black; they are joined by an indistinct, light band, in which are situated a number of gamboge-yellow marks, one on each of segments one and three, and then two marks on segments four to eight. Whereas the anterior marks join the spiracle, the larger posterior mark is oblong and does not touch the spiracle. The head bears black eye-spots.

PUPA (Fig. 17C)

The length of the pupa is generally about 19 mm and usually dark grey, shading to light grey on the underside, except for the head, antennae, and leg position which are a very dark grey. Brownish and green specimens have also been recorded.

Narrow yellow lines run along the keel and the mid-thoracic line. The principal wing veins are marked with black dots.

The whole body is covered with minute black spots and on each segment are somewhat larger, black spots. The latter are situated one to each segment down the dorsal (mid) line and along the lateral keel, on each side of the beak and on the cremaster.

The pupae are fixed in position by the cremaster which is hooked onto a silken pad and by a silken girdle. The abdominal segments can move freely if touched. Hibernation takes place in this stage.

GREEN-VEINED WHITE

Pieris napi subspecies *britannica* Müller & Kautz, 1939

This is probably Ireland's most common butterfly, being found practically everywhere. It is a very variable species bearing heavily marked veins. The adult is to be seen during May and June (sometimes too at the end of April) and again at the end of July and during August. There are two broods in the year. The winter is passed in the pupal stage.

ADULT (Fig. 18D, Plate I H,J)
This butterfly measures about 50 mm across the outstretched wings in both sexes and the ground colour is white with a faintly yellowish-white tinge. However, it is a very variable butterfly in ground colour as well as in intensity of markings.

In the male of the spring brood the forewings, the veins and the costal margin are light grey, somewhat more broadly near the base of the wings. On the underside the apical area of the forewing and the whole of the hindwing is yellow, with the veins of the hindwings covered with black scales giving a green appearance. In the summer brood the veins are more strongly marked on the upper side and sometimes there is an additional black spot similar to that of the female.

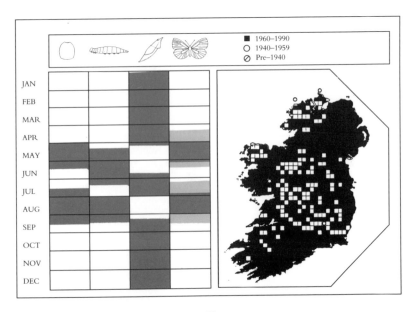

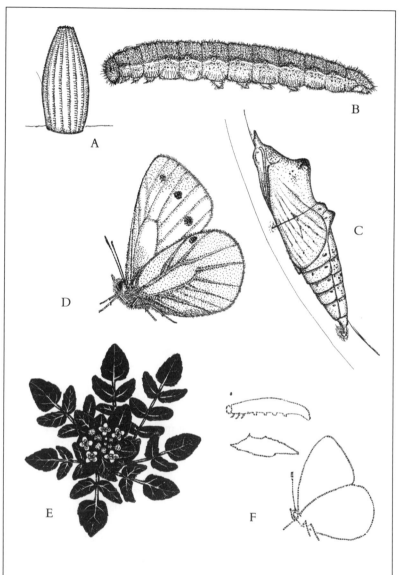

Fig. 18

Green-veined White: A - Egg (ht. about 1mm); B - Larva (L
25.5mm); C - Pupa (L 20mm); D - Adult, side-view (wing-span
50mm); E - Food plant: Watercress, *Nasturtium officinale*;
F - Life size.

In the female, the spring brood has a more creamish ground colour and the veins are more pronounced. There is also an additional black spot adjacent to the bar on the lower margin and there is a tendency for the spots to coalesce. On the underside, the ground colour is lemon-yellow and the outer veins are only faintly marked with grey.

The female of the summer brood is usually more pronounced in marking, often with additional spots, although much fainter on the underside.

There is great variation, however, and occasionally specimens are seen with a bright yellow ground colour, but having dark grey veins with the wings heavily dusted with grey scales.

EGG (Fig. 18A)
About 1 mm in height and at first pale yellow, it later becomes greenish and just before the emergence of the larva changes to a glistening white. The egg is conical in shape and stands erect, adhering to the underside of the leaves of various cruciferous plants (including lady's smock, *Cardamine pratensis*, and garlic mustard, *Alliaria petiolata*) by its base, the plant having been selected by the female and on which the larvae feed. There are about 15 longitudinal ridges of which about 10 extend the whole length of the egg and the remainder originate a little below the crown but run to the base. In between these ridges there are about 45 transverse, minute ribs. This stage lasts from 3 to 5 days. Unlike most butterflies, this species will lay eggs in captivity without difficulty.

LARVA (Fig. 18B)
When first hatched, the young larva is about 1.3 mm in length with a dispro-portionately large, light-brown head and a rather hairy, pale-yellow body. After the fourth moult, when it is fully grown, it measures 25.5 mm in length and, when walking, which it does in a gliding manner whilst moving the head from side to side, it is more slender at the anterior and posterior ends. Each segment is divided into a number of transverse ridges with those in the middle of the body having six. The conspicuous black spiracles are encircled by bright yellow. The whole body is hairy with the hairs on the dorsal surface arising from black tubercles except for a small number, usually 3, on each segment which are black, but arise from white tubercles. Many of the larger hairs bear a globule of a clear liquid at their tip.

It is easy to rear the larvae on a bunch of watercress, *nasturium officinale* tightly wedged into the neck of a jar of water.

PUPA (Fig. 18C)
This measures from 19–21 mm in length, and as well as being held by a cre-master fastened to a silken pad, it is held in position by a silken girdle around its

middle. There is a great variation in ground colour and also in the extent and intensity of black spotting. Generally ground colour is light green, but may be yellowish, buff, or, as in one specimen reared by the author, may be only very light buff shading to white with spotting absent. Colour appears to be more or less influenced by background. (The latter specimen was attached to a piece of perspex.) The shape is much like that of the Small White. The head bears a pronounced, single beak and there is a conspicuous crest on the thorax in the mid-dorsal line. It is acute-angled and even in the lightest-coloured specimens is always more darkly coloured. The line of the crest continues along the abdomen to the anal segment. In addition, a crest originates at the anal angle of the wing-cases on each side, and runs down to the anal segment. There are two projections, the hinder one being the larger, and each bears dark marks at their apices. The pupa can wriggle the abdomen sideways.

The pupal stage may last as little as 12 days, but as winter is passed in this stage by the final brood of the year, it may take about 8 months.

ORANGE-TIP

Anthocharis cardamines subspecies *hibernica*
(Williams, 1916)

One of the attractive sights in spring and early summer is to see the Orange-tip butterflies flying along the lanes and hedges. Only the male possesses the orange tip. The adult is on the wing during late April, May, and early June, and there is one brood annually. The Orange-tip is locally common throughout Ireland.

The larval food plants belong to the CRUCIFERAE and include, especially lady's smock, *Cardamine pratensis*, hedge mustard, *Sisymbrium officinale*, garlic mustard, *Alliaria petiolata*, rockcress, *Arabis* spp., horse radish, *Cochlearia armoracia*, dame's violet, *Hesperis matronalis* and watercress, *Nasturtium officinale*.

The winter is passed in the pupal stage.

ADULT (Fig. 19D, Plate I K,L)
In both sexes the outstretched wings measure about 46 mm but the largest may reach 50 mm and small specimens are frequently encountered measuring only 40 mm. The ground colour is white and the bases of the wings are black but the most easily distinguishing feature, at least in the male, is a large rounded

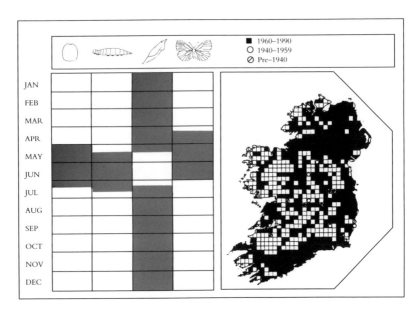

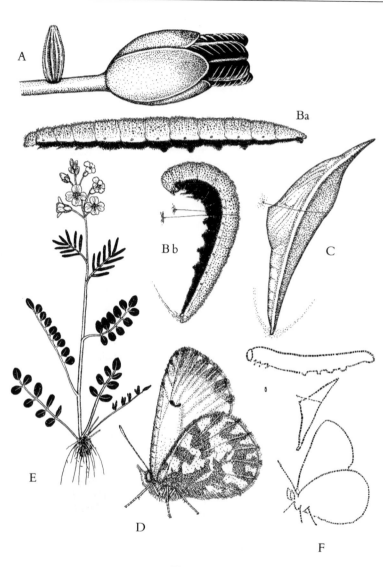

Fig. 19

Orange Tip: A - Egg (ht. 1.2mm); Ba - Larva (L 30mm); Bb -
Larva in pupating position; C - Pupa (L 19mm); D - Adult, side-
view (wing span 46mm; E - Food plant: Lady's smock,
Cardamine pratensis; F - Life size.

orange patch at the apex of the forewings with a black, lunate tip to the wings which is smaller in the male than in the female. There is a lunate black spot at the outer edge of the discoidal cell which is larger in the female. On the underside the hindwings are chequered with green, more or less rectangular, patches. The green colouration is brought about by mixtures of yellow and black scales and the patterning shows through to the upper side.

EGG (Fig. 19A)

Like all species in the PIERIDAE, the egg of the Orange-Tip is elongated. It measures about 1.2 mm in height, and skittle-shaped, being widest at about the middle, and the top is rounded. There are about 18 longitudinal ridges of which 12 reach from the base to the apex, the remainder terminating just a little short of the apex. There are about 40 transverse ribs. When first laid the egg is white tinged with greenish-yellow but it gradually turns deep orange until finally, just before hatching, it becomes pale brown. The egg stage lasts about 7 days and, on hatching, the larva eats the egg shell and any unhatched eggs or other recently emerged larvae which it chances upon.

The eggs are deposited singly, most often one on each plant and egg-laying females generally avoid a plant on which an egg has already been laid. They can be seen to flutter to the plant, then, without settling, fly off again. The egg is usually laid either on the calyx or on the stalk just below it and with a little practice, the keen-eyed human observer can detect it from a distance of half a metre or so!

LARVA (Fig. 19Ba, Bb)

On hatching, the young larva is yellowish-brown, and on examination with a lens is shown to be liberally furnished with small black warts. When fully grown it measures about 30 mm in length, is generally slender, and slightly attenuated at both ends. Each segment is sub-divided into about 7 which gives the larva a wrinkled appearance on the upper surface but the sub-divisions are absent below the spiracles. The under surface is much less curved than the upper. The ground colour of the upper surface is green with a bluish tinge but shades into white on each side, giving a frosted appearance, and the spiracles are situated in the white stripe. The whole of the under surface is a rich bottle-green. The body is completely covered with black warts except for some on the white stripe which are white. Each wart bears a bristle, the longest of which (on the back) are divided at the tip and carry a bead of clear fluid. The head is similar in colour to that of the body and bears warts and bristles. The larva generally rests in a straight position when it closely resembles a seed pod.

PUPA (Fig. 19C)

The larva prepares for pupation by spinning a pad of silk which is then gripped by the anal claspers and then a girdle of silk is spun round its middle. It is then strongly curved with the head touching the surface to which the hind end is attached. When pupation takes place a narrow-angled keel, formed by the wing cases, touches the pupation surface and the head region is elongated to form a conspicuous beak, whilst the abdominal region is long and attenuated. The whole pupa forms a narrow crescent pointing away from the pupation surface, with the white lateral line, similar to that of the larva, giving the appearance of a seed pod. It is from 18-20 mm in length, which is rather smaller than English specimens. The colour is at first green with white markings, but after a few days it commences to change to light brown. Colour, however, is variable and in some cases the green colour persists throughout the pupal stage. Generally, though, the pupa assumes various shades from light buff to dark brown and is usually darker on the upper surface with the beak usually much darker, but the light-coloured, lateral stripe persists. The pupal stage lasts from the end of June or beginning of July to the following end of April or beginning of May (usually about 10 months).

FAMILY LYCAENIDAE

The family LYCAENIDAE is several thousand species strong and of world-wide distribution. They are generally small. Species of three sub-families occur in Ireland. These are the Hairstreaks, THECLINAE, the Coppers, LYCAENINAE, and the Blues, POLYOMMATINAE. The adults are usually brilliantly (interference) coloured, especially those in the two latter sub-families although the females are often of a more subdued colouration. The undersides of the wings are often spotted and there are sometimes tail-like extensions to the hindwings. The adults possess six walking legs. The larvae are wood louse-shaped, crawl very slowly and are able to retract the head into the first thoracic segment.

SUB-FAMILY: THECLINAE

Members of the sub-family THECLINAE are commonly known as Hair-streaks, and Ireland is host to three species. They are rather small in size but of robust appearance. Usually the ground colour of the upper surface of the wings is very sombre but the undersides are pale or very bright. The hind-wings often bear a short 'tail'.

The larvae are slow-moving, the head often protracted under or within the prothoracic segment, which is enlarged and generally disc-like. The interseg-mental grooves are prominent and deep, and this gives the larva a most un-caterpillar-like appearance as often the legs are hidden by a fringe of hairs on the extended lateral lobes. There is great variation in the length of the egg stage. Whereas in the Green Hairstreak this stage lasts only for about a week, in the Brown and the Purple Hairstreak the stage lasts throughout the winter, commonly taking nine months. All the Irish Hairstreaks are single-brooded.

GREEN HAIRSTREAK

Callophrys rubi (Linnaeus, 1758)

This is a most attractive little butterfly which occurs in a variety of locality types from woodland edges, hedges, rough hills and scrub covered moorland. The larval food plants are therefore varied and amongst them are broom, *Sarothamnus scoparius*, gorse, *Ulex europaeus*, bird's foot trefoil, *Lotus corniculatus*, bilberry, *Vaccinium myrtillus*, bramble and *Rubus* spp., (buds only).

It is single-brooded and the adult is generally seen in May and June. Winter is passed in the pupal stage.

The male is often aggressive in defending its territory against other butterflies and will sometimes even buffet human beings!

The Green Hairstreak is widely distributed, although local, but in some parts of the south and west of Ireland it is exceptionally common.

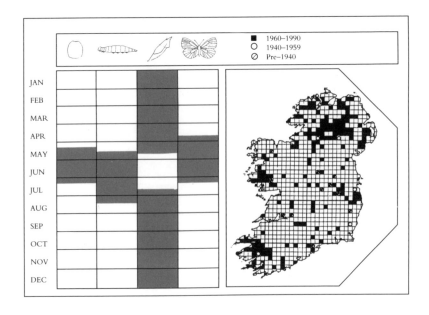

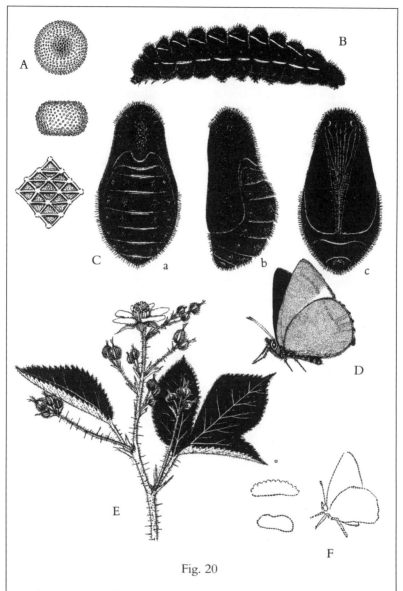

Fig. 20

Green Hairstreak: A - Egg (dia. 0.65mm): a- view from above,
b-side-view, c-surface highly magnified; B - Larva (L 16mm);
C - Pupa (L 8.5mm) a-view from above, b-side-view, c-view
from below; D - Adult, side-view (wing-span 33mm); E - Food
plant; Bramble, *Rubus Spp.*; F - Life size.

ADULT (Fig. 20D, Plate I M,N)

In both sexes the outstretched wings measure about 33 mm. When freshly emerged the ground colour is brown with a rich, golden-bronze sheen.

In the male there is an oval patch of androconial scales at the upper corner of the discoidal cell, turning to grey when the scent scales have been lost. There is a tuft of black scales at the anal angle of the hindwing. There is a white fringe to the hindwings marked with black opposite the veins, whilst that of the forewings is dark.

Except for the androconial scale patch, the sexes are similar. The underside is bright green, except for a thin edge of greyish-brown very near the margin of the hindwings and some white spots variable in number in a transverse row across the wings, although those of the forewings are usually few and faint.

EGG (Fig. 20Aa,b,c)

This is laid singly on either a flower bud or a terminal shoot of the larval food plant. In shape it is spheroidal but flattened at the top and bottom. There is a small depression at the top. It is about 0.65 mm in diameter but is less than this in height. In colour the egg is a light green for the first few days but later becomes light grey. The whole surface is covered with a reticulated pattern of minute projections joined together with shallow ridges, giving the appearance of frosted glass.

LARVA (Fig. 20B)

Like all the 'Hairstreaks' and most of the Lycaenids, the Green Hairstreak larva is slug-like in general shape and in its slow-moving behaviour. When full-grown it is about 16 mm in length, and the ground colour is bright apple-green. Viewed from the side there is a lateral, lemon-yellow band commencing at the third thoracic segment, and a series of oblique stripes, of the same colour, situated dorsally. The segments are bulbous, which result in the inter-segmented grooves being well-defined, and the whole body is covered with reddish-brown spines. Viewed from the top there is a dark, central band and a series of triangular lobes edged with the oblique, lemon-yellow stripes seen laterally. The segments at the anterior end and posterior end are flattened. The shiny head is small and generally held retracted, or partially so, into the first thoracic segment. In colour it is pale brown with a transverse, pearlish-white band, and the eye-spots are conspicuous. The feet of the abdominal legs are divided with a patch of minute hooks at the front and the back. It is of interest to note the presence of a gland on the back of the 10th segment, similar to that present in the sub-family LYCAENINAE, which in some species is known to attract ants.

The larvae are stated to be cannibalistic, but this was not the case with those reared by the writer. Seven pupae resulted from seven eggs, although the larvae were often seen to be feeding close to each other. Four pupated together under one small piece of moss.

PUPA (Figs. 20Ca,b,c)

The pupa lies freely amongst the litter and moss at the base of the food plant, not secured in any way, but with a few fine silk threads loosely fastening the moss fronds and loose debris together over it.

It varies in length from 8-9 mm (but is regarded as reaching 9.5 mm) and is from about 4.2-4.8 mm across the widest part of the abdomen. There is no better general description for the shape of the pupa than that of Frohawk, who wrote that it was 'stout, rounded and dumpy'. Viewed from above, the rounded head region meets the thorax obtusely at an angle and the abdomen is then much dilated. Viewed laterally, the ventral outline is almost straight, which accentuates the appearance of the swollen abdomen. The surface of the pupa (except the wing and limb regions) is clothed with reddish-brown spines, mostly of uniform length. The conspicuous spiracles are also reddish-brown. From the ventral aspect it is seen that the outer margins of the wing-cases are almost transverse, and the tips of the antennae almost meet the anal extremity. The entire surface of the cuticle is covered with a fine reticulation.

For the first day or so, the colour of the thoracic region is bright apple green, with the abdomen yellowish with a central dark-green stripe running longitudinally along the thorax and abdomen. It soon becomes much darker, finally turning to a reddish-brown ground colour mottled with black. The pupal stage lasts from the beginning of July until the following May—at least 10 months.

BROWN HAIRSTREAK

Thecla betulae (Linnaeus, 1758)

The Brown Hairstreak is Ireland's most rare Hairstreak. It may also be Ireland's rarest resident butterfly species. Most Brown Hairstreaks have been recorded as larvae beaten from sloe (blackthorn) bushes on to a white sheet or 'beating tray'. This species is single-brooded.

ADULT (Fig. 21D, Plate I O,P)
The distance across the expanded wings is about 38 mm in the male and about 42 mm in the female. Males and females are quite different on the upper side, although òn the underside they are so similar as to be indistinguishable. In the male the upperside is blackish-brown with a faint, greyish suffusion. On the forewing there is a prominent, black bar at the outer edge of the discal cell and a pale orange colour outwards of this. On the outer edge of the hind wings there are two orange marks, one at the anal angle and one on the 'tail'. In the female the upper surface ground colour lacks the greyish tinge, but beyond the black bar there is a wide and very conspicuous orange band, and the orange

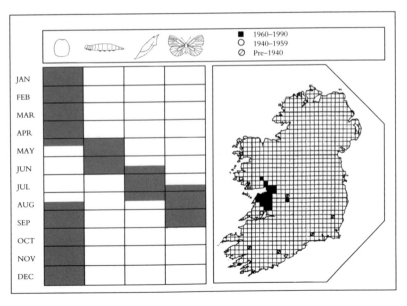

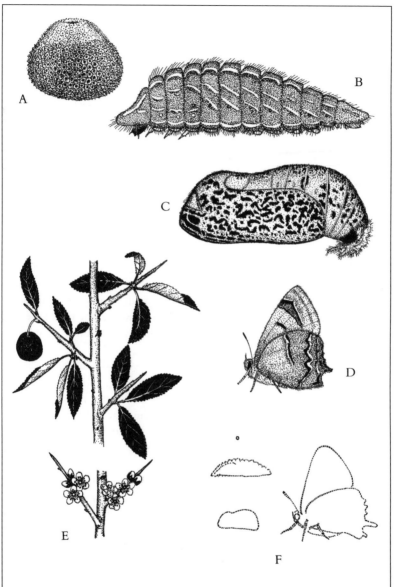

Fig. 21

Brown Hairstreak: A - Egg (dia. 0.65mm); B - Larva (L 17mm);
C - Pupa (L 12mm); D - Adult, side-view (wing-span m. 38mm,
f. 42mm); E - Food plant: Blackthorn, *Prunus spinosa*; F - Life size

spots on the outer margin of the hindwings are usually three in number, although there are only two on occasion.

The underside of both sexes is light-brown shading to reddish on the outer margins, but this is rather more orange in the female. There is a black bar edged with white in the forewings, and two bars on the hindwing (the outer being longer and wavy and in the shape of a W near the anal angle) in both sexes. In the female the anal angle bears a V-shaped mark with a crescent-shaped mark adjacent. These are only faint in the male.

EGG (Fig. 21A)

The eggs are laid singly on the twigs of blackthorn (sloe), *Prunus spinosa*, near a dormant bud, and in this position they remain for seven months before hatching at the end of March or the beginning of April. The blackthorn bush selected by the female for egg-laying is generally a rather stumpy shrub on the outside of a clump.

The egg is about 0.65 mm in diameter; the height is approximately 0.6 mm. There is a slight constriction about one-third of the height from the top and this top third of the egg is somewhat different in appearance from the basal two-thirds. The whole surface is covered with a vaguely pentagonal reticulation, and the micropyle is located in a depression at the top of the egg. It is pearly-white in colour, but just before hatching is greenish at the top.

LARVA (Fig. 21B)

The full-grown larva is 17 mm in length, generally spindle-shaped, with deep intersegmental grooves. The ventral surface is flat and, as the mid-dorsal line is crested, the caterpillar is roughly triangular in transverse section. The prothorax is triangular with a small excision at the apex. When at rest the dark brown and blackish head is retracted under the prothorax.

PUPA (Fig. 21C)

The pupa of the Brown Hairstreak is stout and dumpy with no angular projections, and is about 12 mm in length. The female pupae are larger than the males. The rounded head region is continuous with the thoracic area, wherein the base of the wings is shoulder-like and also rounded. The abdomen is thicker and curves downwards towards the anal extremity which is generally covered by the larval skin. However, if the latter is removed, a group of spines is revealed which takes the place of a cremastral hook found in many butterfly species. Many parts of the pupal cuticle bear thickened, bristle-like hairs, but the wing-cases are devoid of such. The general ground colour is brownish, but overall blotched and speckled with a dull, darkish purplish-brown. These marks form bands in the antennal and leg region on the ventral surface. The pale brown spiracles are prominent. Microscopically the cuticle can be seen to be finely reticulated. The pupal stage lasts a little in excess of three weeks.

There seems to be some doubt as to whether the pupa is held by a girdle in addition to the larval skin. Certainly the specimen reared by the author bore a very fine thread of silk although somewhat imperfect. A rather flimsy shelter is formed by the pupa by drawing a few leaves together with fine silken threads.

PURPLE HAIRSTREAK

Quercusia quercus (Linnaeus, 1758)

This is a local species recorded from only three 10 km squares in the North and from twenty-three in the South, post 1960. It is confined to old oak woodland and does not advertise its presence, spending much of its time amongst the higher branches of outstanding trees—not always oak. Here a group will gather and flit around the tree, instantly settling as soon as the sun disappears. Abroad, the Purple Hairstreak occurs throughout Europe except far north.

ADULT (Fig. 22D, Plate I Q,R)
The male of this butterfly measures about 39 mm across the expanded wings, whilst the female is slightly smaller, being about 37 mm. There is a distinctive difference between the sexes in the colouration of the upperside of the wings. In the male the ground colour is a unicolourous 'deep purplish-indigo-blue' with black margins. The forewings of the female are purple-black with a velvet sheen and with two oblong patches of rich, lustrous purple crossed by a black vein at the base. There is a short, black tail tipped with white on the hindwings. The undersides of the wings of both sexes are very different from the upper

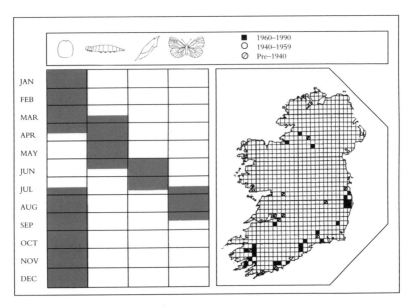

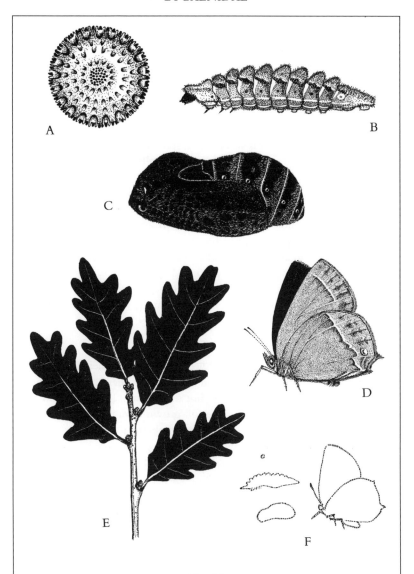

Fig. 22

Purple Hairstreak: A - Egg, view from above (ht. 0.5mm, dia.
0.8mm); B - Larva (L 16mm); C - Pupa (L 10.2mm) D - Adult,
side-view (wing-span m. 39mm, f. 37mm); E - Food plant: Oak,
Quercus robur, F - Life size.

sides. They are pearl-grey, becoming lighter towards the body. On the forewings there is a row of 7 black spots set in a whitish band towards the margin. On the hindwings there are 3 whites tripes, the basal one edged with black and roughly in the shape of a 'W'. There is a small orange and black eye-spot near the black-margined tail.

EGG (Fig. 22A)

The egg is comparatively large, being about 0.50 mm in height and 0.80 mm in diameter. In shape it is compressed; spherical, but rather flatter at the base. When first laid it is bluish-grey but gradually assumes a nearly white colour. The micropyle, shown by a group of dark spots, is at the base of a depression at the apex. As is common to all lycaenids, there is a fine but irregular pattern of cells bounded by ridges. At each intersection of the ridges, there is a pronounced, spike-like protrusion. These protrusions are white and give the appearance of the egg as 'resembling opaque, frosted glass'. The egg is laid at the base of a bud of oak (*Quercus* spp.), usually near the extremity of the twig, during July and August. Hatching does not take place until the following April when the bud begins to expand.

The egg stage lasts about eight months, during which time it remains unprotected on the oak twig.

LARVA (Fig. 22B)

On hatching, the larva finds a way between the opening bracts and begins to bore into the expanding bud, eating out the centre. It then spins a silk thread around the bud so that the bracts do not drop away. The larva exhibits a remarkable resemblance to them. The full-grown larva measures 16 mm in length, and is broad and compressed and resembling a woodlouse in shape. The intersegmental divisions, however, are very pronounced.

The ground colour is light brown, the mid-dorsal longitudinal stripe is black lined with white, whilst the lateral, oblique bars on each segment are a rich brown colour edged with white. The black spiracles are surrounded by a pale area. Below the spiracles is a longitudinal, white bar. There is a shield-shaped plate on the second thoracic segment. The head, which can be retracted within the prothoracic segment, is shining brown. The body surface is covered with dark serrated hairs which have 'light glassy tips', giving the larva a velvety appearance.

The length of the larval stage is about 45 days.

PUPA (Fig. 22C)

When full-grown, the larva spins a few strands of silk to form a hammock under a leaf or on the ground surface amongst moss or litter. The pupa is typically lycaenid, being stout and rounded—but there are no cremastral hooks. The larval skin, however, remains attached to the pupal anal segment. It is 10.2 mm long. Generally rusty-red in colour, the body is spotted and blotched with dark, purplish-brown, although the ventral surface is relatively free from such markings. The head, wings and ventral surfaces are paler in colour. Although the pupa has a rather shiny appearance (except for the wings),the surface is abundantly provided with short, minute spines which are star-shaped at the apex. There is a series of longer branched spines along the spiracular line.

The length of the pupal stage is generally about 4 weeks.

SUB-FAMILY: LYCAENINAE

This subfamily is represented by only one resident species in Ireland; another larger species has been introduced in the past, but no longer occurs here. A number of species occur throughout Europe, known popularly as 'Coppers' on account of their predominant burnished copper colour.

Members of this sub-family differ from other members of the family by the shape of the antennae, in which the 'knob' is rather more abrupt, and the rather differently shaped palpi.

Fig. 23   Family Lycaenidae. Small in size, larva woodlouse-shaped. Sub-family Lycaeninae. Upper surfce brilliant copper-coloured. Small copper, *Lycaena phlaeas.*

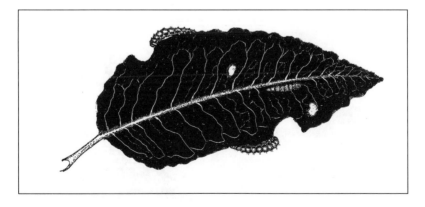

Fig. 24   Larvae of Small copper on leaf of Broad-leaved dock, *Rumex obtusifolius.*

SMALL COPPER

Lycaena phlaeas subspecies *hibernica* (Goodson, 1948)

This small, copper-coloured butterfly aggressively defends its territory with great agility. Any other butterfly entering the Small Copper's own little patch is immediately buffeted away. When accomplished, it returns to its vantage point and sits with outstretched wings ready for the next adversary! Its flight is exceptionally fast and difficult to follow.

There are generally two life cycles annually, but a third generation in favourable conditions is possible. It is widely distributed but like many Irish butterflies, however, its recorded distribution is most concentrated where observers are most numerous.

The Small Copper frequently introduces itself to the observer on the flower-heads of COMPOSITAE, to which it is very attracted—such as the fleabane, *Pulicaria dysenterica*, and Michaelmas daisy found in gardens.

ADULT (Fig. 25D, Plate II A)

In the male the outstretched wings measure 32 mm; 35 mm in the female. The forewings of the male are rather narrower, with the outer margin somewhat straighter than those of the female. The ground colour of the

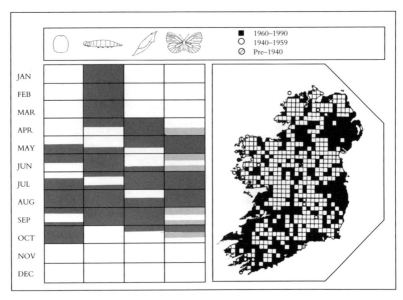

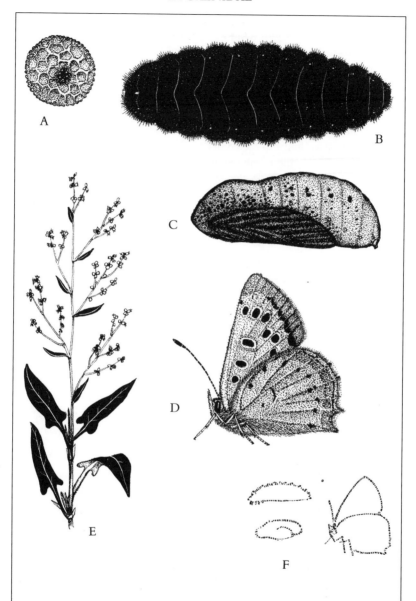

Fig. 25   Small Copper: A - Egg, view from above (dia 0.6mm);
B - Larva (L 16mm); C - Pupa (L 10.5mm); D - Adult, side-
view (wing-span m. 32mm, f.35mm); E - Food plant: Common
sorrel, *Rumex acetosa*; F - Life size.

forewings is a brilliant shining coppery-orange with a broad, blackish-brown outer margin. The copper-coloured area is spotted with black, roughly square markings. The hindwings are bronze-black with a broad scalloped band of copper near the margin.

The sexes are similar. The underside of the forewings are pale orange and spotted with black, as on the upper surface, but with some additional marks. The outer margin, as well as the whole of the hindwing, is a light greyish-brown. On the latter are located a number of small, black spots, with a border of red lunar marks similar to the border on the upper surface. The Irish form of the species is distinct and is referred to as the subspecies *hibernica*.

There are two or three broods annually. The third brood may result from eggs laid in early August; the larvae feeding up during a warm, sunny September, and adults emerging during late September and early October. The larvae generally hibernate during the winter months. Because of this, the length of the life cycle is very variable—from as little as 30 days to as much as about 145 days.

EGG (Fig. 25A)

This is circular and about 0.60 mm in diameter when viewed from above, but it is compressed and bean-shaped in side view, measuring in height only about 0.30 mm. It is flattened at the base where it adheres to the food plant, and the summit is slightly concave where the micropyle is situated. The egg is covered with ridges in a reticulate, irregular honeycomb pattern; the cells near the upper surface being mainly pentagonal, whilst those on the sides are hexagonal. The ridges are highest at their intersections. It is whitish and porcelain-like with a delicate texture, whilst the micropyle is dark green. The eggs are laid singly on the food plant. This stage lasts about 6 days.

LARVA (Fig. 25B)

The newly-hatched larva feeds on the underside of the leaves of its food plant, making a small groove in which it lies. A number of grooves are constructed until after the second moult, when portions of the entire leaf are consumed. The food plants are broad-leaved dock, *Rumex obtusifolius*, common sorrel, *Rumex acetosa*, sheep's sorrel, *Rumex acetosella*, and no doubt other species of the genus *Rumex*.

There is considerable variation in the colour of the larvae. Some are uniformly light-green, whilst others are a somewhat darker green with a lilac-pink, mid-dorsal stripe, and a line of the same colour running along the entire length of the sides of the larva and joining at the front and back. The undersurface and legs may be pink or pale pink also.

The head is usually not visible from the top, being small, olive-brown patterned with black, and completely covered by the first thoracic segment.

LYCAENIDAE

At the centre of the pronotum is a gland-like, pale-coloured pit, and the spiracles are very light-brown to orange in colour. The whole body surface is covered with minute white warts and small, reddish-brown, bristle-like hairs. The length of the fully grown larva is slightly less than 16 mm. When viewed from the rear the larva is triangular in shape and is hump-backed with the legs hardly discernible. It moves extraordinarily slowly.

PUPA (Fig. 25C)

This is approximately 11 mm in length and is stout, dumpy and rounded in form. The head is only slightly angled and is then confluent with the thorax, which rises dorsally before becoming constricted where it joins the abdomen. The wing cases project forwards at the shoulder, touching the prothoracic spiracle. The ground colour is a light, brownish yellow with a slight greenish tinge. It is finely speckled with dark brown and spotted with black longitudinally. A dark brown streak runs down the centre of the back, marked with a black spot on each abdominal segment. The antennae and proboscis are black. The wing cases are dark brown, with the position of the veins pale. The cremaster is small. The spiracles are white and buff. The surface of the head and thorax is liberally sprinkled with minute white tulip-shaped processes, as is the abdomen, and these are only just discernible with a x10 lens. The pupa is held in position by the cremastral hooks caught in a pad of silk with a fine silk thread around the 'waist'.

The length of the pupal stage varies between 25 to 30 days when the larva has over-wintered, but is shorter in the summer broods.

SUB-FAMILY: POLYOMMATINAE

Three of Ireland's butterflies belong to this sub-family. They are easily differentiated from the other closely related sub-families, and are characterized by the blue colouration, especially in the males, of the upper surface of the wings and by the spotted undersurfaces. This spotting is extremely variable within the species. Compared with the Holly and the Common Blue, the Small Blue could be considered drab in that the upper sides of the wings are mainly brown with often only a sprinkling of bright blue scales. Many of the European species of this subfamily have larvae which feed on species of LEGUMINOSAE, but among the Irish species the Holly Blue is the odd one out in this case. Five species common in continental Europe have sometimes been caught in southern England. It is not then unreasonable to suppose that they may be recorded sometime from Ireland.

SMALL BLUE

Cupido minimus (Fuessly, 1775)

The Small Blue is a very local insect in Ireland, mainly found on coastal dune systems and also some calcareous regions further inland. Where it occurs, it is generally abundant.

ADULT (Fig. 26D, Plate II B,C)
This is Ireland's smallest butterfly. Whereas large specimens may reach 28 mm across the wings, specimens often measure only 20 mm. The sexes are easily distinguished. In the male the upper side is smokey-black with the basal half powdered with silvery blue. The ground colour of the underside is pearl-grey shading to pale blue at the base. In the centre of the wing is a white-edged, black bar-shaped mark, and towards the outer margin is a series of 7 similar spots arranged in a curve. The hindwing is rather similar, but there are 9 dots and the curve is broken.

In the female the upper side is dark, bronze-brown, and entirely lacking in blue scales. The underside is tinged with light brown.

EGG (Fig. 26A)
The eggs are deposited singly on the hairy calyx of a flower of kidney vetch, *Anthyllis vulneraria*. This may be from the end of May until July according to

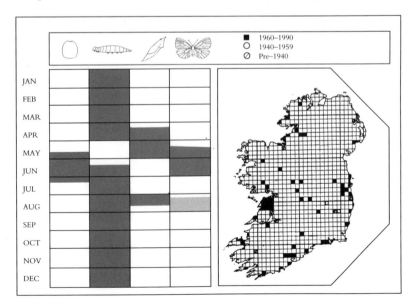

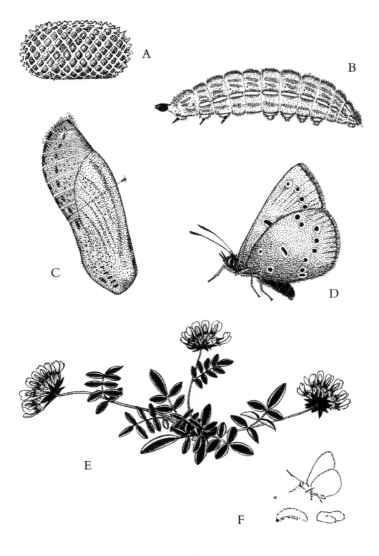

Fig. 26

Small Blue: A - Egg (ht. 0.2mm, dia. 0.4mm); B - Larva (L 9.5mm); C - Pupa (L 8mm); D - Adult, side-view (wing-span 20-28mm); E - Food plant: Kidney vetch, *Anthyllis vulneraria*; F - Life size.

weather conditions. The egg is very small and is generally hidden. Only 0.2 mm in height and 0.4 mm in diameter, it is a flattened spheroid in shape. The micropyle in the centre of the upper surface is not situated in a depression, as is commonly the case, but is dark in colour. The ground colour of the egg is a pale, bluish-green, but the whole surface is reticulated with a fine network of irregular rhomboid cells, formed by white ridges, and their prominence gives the egg a white appearance. Where the ridges meet there is a knob-like protrusion.

The egg stage lasts from 5 to 7 days.

LARVA (Fig. 26B)

Immediately on hatching the larva bores its way through the wall of the calyx into the developing ovule of the food plant. (In captivity it will tunnel into a green pea.) Towards the end of July it becomes full-grown and is about 9.5 mm in length. Like all lycaenid larvae it is woodlouse-shaped, and the very small black shiny head may be extended forward to a considerable length during its slow, slug-like progression or, on the other hand, it may be retracted entirely within the prothorax.

There is wide variation in colour. When newly emerged the larva is pale yellow, and some larvae stay this colour during the whole larval stage. Others assume a greenish tinge, although the more usual colour is pale brown. All are marked, however, with pink to a greater or lesser degree, with a longitudinal mid-dorsal stripe and a pair of oblique stripes on each segment. In addition there is a lateral band below the spiracle on each side which is white, edged with pink.

When fully fed, the larva binds a few dead calyces together with silk and hibernates amongst them. The larval markings become fainter and practically disappear whilst it remains motionless for about 10 months.

Frohawk (1924) remarked on the startling resemblance of the hibernating larva to the dead flower of kidney vetch, and he thought it to be such a perfect example of protective resemblance as to render it almost invisible.

PUPA (Fig. 26C)

The comparatively stout pupa measures about 8 mm in length, and is attached by cremastral hooks to a silken pad and girdle around the middle. In outline it is rounded, the head being hidden by the projecting prothorax. The wing-cases are rather swollen and the anal segment is rounded. In the lateral view the ventral surface is straight, with the cremastral hooks arising in a curved line on the ventral surface of the anal segment.

The ground colour is from grey to creamy-buff. Head, thorax and wing-cases are spotted and striped with dusky-brown. On the wing cases this colouring occurs between the veins and forms a stripe along the mid-dorsal line of the thorax. This line continues along the abdomen as a series of black spots. A secondary row occurs on each side—as a series of blotches on the thorax and as a series of small black dots on the abdomen. The whole body is covered with long, thin but bristle-like hairs, each arising from a swollen base. Mention should be made of the presence of a honey gland (occurring in the larva also) which is situated on the seventh abdominal segment.

The pupal stage is from 15 to 16 days.

COMMON BLUE

Polyommatus icarus subspecies *mariscolore* (Kane, 1893)

This is one of Ireland's most widely distributed and abundant butterflies, especially in coastal regions. It is single-brooded in the north-west and north, although the flight period extends from June to mid-August. In the west and south it is double-brooded. This butterfly occurs almost anywhere where its food plant, bird's foot trefoil, *Lotus corniculatus*, grows. Rest harrow, *Ononis repens*, is another larval food plant. The winter is passed as a young larva.

ADULT (Fig. 27D, Plate II D,E)
The average length across the outstretched wings is about 35 mm in both sexes.

The male is light, shining blue, shot with violet or mauve. There is a narrow, white edge to the front margin whilst the outer margins of the fore- and hindwings are outlined with black. The white fringes are divided by a fine grey line. On the underside the forewings are grey, lightly dusted with silvery-blue at the base. There are two white eye-spots with black pupils between the discoidal spot and the base of the wing, and a series of six

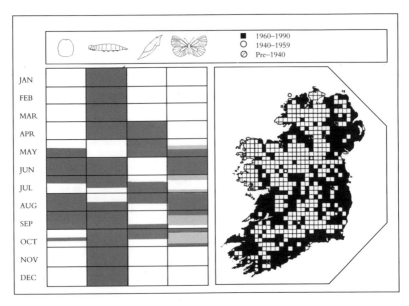

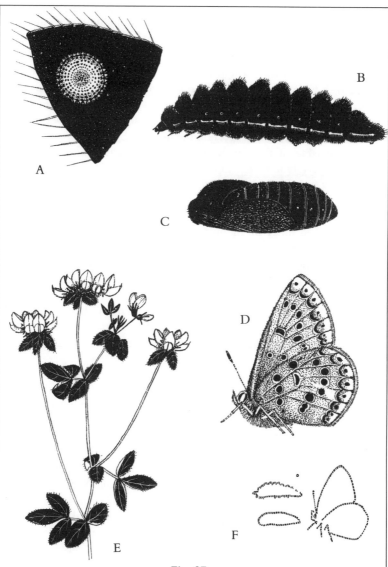

Fig. 27

Common Blue: A - Egg, view from above (dia. 0.6mm); B - Larva
(L 12.5mm); C - Pupa (L 10.5mm) D - Adult, side-view wing-
span 35mm); E - Food plant: Bird's foot trefoil, *Lotus corniculatus*;
F - Life size.

similar eye-spots followed by a series of six orange spots near the margin with black and white crescents on each side. The hindwing is somewhat similar except that the blue dusting is more extensive, there being about 12 black-pupilled eye-spots with eight orange spots near the margin in addition.

The female is easily distinguished from the male. It is dusky-brown suffused with violet-blue towards the base of the wings to a greater or lesser extent. Close to the margins there are series of dark orange crescents bordered by a black lunule on the inner side and a black bar on the outer side of the forewing and with black spots on the hindwing.

The underside of the female is light brown, with only the slightest dusting of silvery-blue near the base—if present at all. The orange spots are usually larger and more pronounced.

EGG (Fig. 27A)

The eggs are laid singly on the upper surface of a leaflet of the food plant, usually near the apex, and are about 0.60 mm in diameter. They are spheroidal in shape but compressed at the top and bottom, being slightly indented at the top, which is the position of the micropyle. The upper surface is covered with a raised, reticulated (but somewhat irregular) pattern of minute projections which are connected by ridges. The whole effect is that of lacework. Nearer the base, however, the pattern disappears and the surface is smooth. The ground colour of the egg is greenish-grey whilst the reticulated pattern is white. This stage lasts about 9 days.

LARVA (Fig. 27B)

The larva becomes fully-grown after the fourth moult when it is between 12 and 13 mm in length. The general shape is squat, slug-like and oval when viewed from above. In side view, whilst the first, tenth and eleventh segments are flattened and almost spade-like, the remaining segments are strongly lobed, the intersegmental grooves being deep. The shiny black head is very small and is visible only whilst the larva is feeding. When resting it is entirely withdrawn into the first thoracic segment.

There is a honey gland on the upper surface of the tenth segment and behind the spiracle on the eleventh segment there is a retractile tubercle. Whitish hairs are present, all mounted on minute tubercles, those on the top of the back and on the side ridges being longest. There is a gland-like, pale-coloured plate on the first thoracic segment. Larvae collected by the author from bird's foot trefoil on a grass-topped wall were attended by black ants.

The general ground colour is a rich green and there is a darker, longitudinal stripe down the centre of the upper surface and a greenish-white longitudinal stripe along the sides. The spiracles are white and the legs a brownish-yellow. On the upper surface of the tenth segment is a reddish-brown mark.

There is great variation in the length of the larval stage. This may be only a few weeks when the eggs are laid at the end of May or early June, but may last for many months if the larvae overwinter.

PUPA (Fig. 27C)

When about to pupate on the surface of the ground, the larva spins a few silken strands, fastening the stem and lower leaves of its food plant together. The resulting pupa is not attached but lies freely on the ground amongst the litter. It is about 9.5-11.5 mm in length and is at first translucent. The head is rounded and prominent and the thoracic region somewhat waisted at its junction with the abdomen, which is swollen. The last three segments of the abdomen reduce in size abruptly. In colour the head is brownish-buff, with the thorax and abdomen green and the wing-cases pale brown. Over the whole body there is a fine reticulated pattern and, with the exception of the areas of the antennae and wings, there is a covering of minute white bristles. There are some branched hairs arising from brown tubercles on the head and adjacent to the spiracle on the sixth abdominal segment. Two days before adult emergence the colour darkens and becomes opaque, the wings assuming a dark, leaden colour. The pupal stage lasts about 2 weeks.

HOLLY BLUE

Celastrina argiolus subspecies *britanna* (Verity, 1919)

Of Ireland's three species of 'Blue' butterflies the Holly Blue can usually be recognized from a distance by its purposeful, but fluttering, flight around holly bushes during April and May at about two to ten metres from the ground. In addition, it may sometimes be seen as a second brood in July and August, but in this case flying around ivy. Baynes (1964) considered that it is single-brooded in the northern half of Ireland and double-brooded in the southern. He suggested, however, that the tendency to produce a second generation in Ireland is of recent development and is spreading northwards. Winter is passed as a pupa.

In its distribution the Holly Blue is local, but it is usually found not far away from the coast in areas where there are remnants of old woodland. It seems to have disappeared from a number of inland localities, however this more likely reflects the lack of recent field observations in such areas.

ADULT (Fig. 28D, Plate II F,G)
Length across the expanded wings is about 35 mm. In both sexes the ground colour of the upper surfaces of the wings is a light, delicate blue-tinged lilac. There is a distinct sexual difference, however, in the amount of black edging on the forewing. In the male, there is only a narrow black edge to the margin, decreasing in width from the apex to the inner angle. In the female

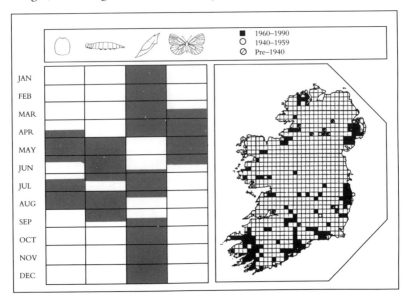

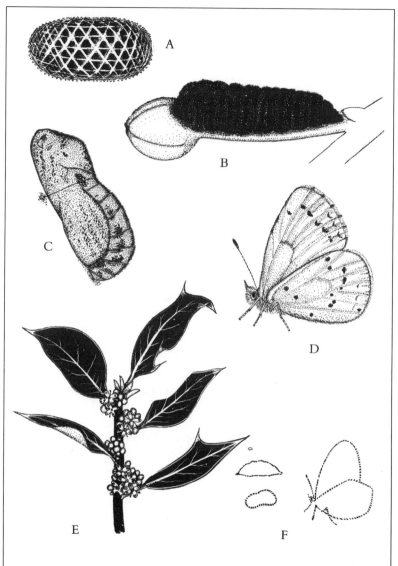

Fig. 28

Holly Blue: A - Egg (ht. 0.3mm, dia. 0.6mm); B - Larva
(L 15mm) C - Pupa (L 8.5mm); D - Adult, side-view (wing-
span 35mm); E - Food plant: Holly, *Ilex aquifolium* (also ivy, *Hedera
helix)*; F - Life size.

this edging is wide and extends around the apex and the outer margin. In the male, the hindwing has a thin, black line around the margin, whereas in the female, there is much more black around the costal margin, as well as a series of black, crescent-shaped marks along the sub-marginal area.

The ground colour of the underside of both sexes is a pale, silvery blue. In the male there is a faint black streak at the end of the discoidal cell and fine black marks arranged in a crescent about midway between the streak and the outer margin of the wing. Near the latter there is a series of faint marks. On the hindwing (underside) there are about twelve black spots scattered more or less in the central area of the wing. The female underside is generally similar, but more heavily marked.

EGG (Fig. 28A)

The egg is disc-shaped and about 0.6 mm in diameter and only about 0.3 mm in height. The micropyle at the centre of the upper surface is situated in a pit-like depression and is finely punctured. The whole surface of the egg is covered with a delicate pattern of raised reticulations resembling lace. About six ribs radiate from prominent protrusions. The cells so-formed are largest around the centre and diminish towards the top and the base. Frohawk describes the ground colour as a 'delicate, pale, greenish-blue' and the reticulations as 'pure white and glossy, resembling the finest white porcelain'. The egg stage lasts about a week.

LARVA (Fig. 28B)

The fully grown larva is up to nearly 15 mm in length and is typically lycaenid in shape, rather stout but diminishing towards the head and more so towards the hinder end. The intersegmental grooves are pronounced. The shining dark head is retractile, extending forwards on a light-coloured, neck-like region when the larva is feeding or exploring, but pulled back under the compressed prothorax when resting or when disturbed. The head is often moved about restlessly.

Frohawk recognised three colour forms after the second moult and immediately before the third moult: -

1. Ground colour clear green with dull, pinkish-purple markings; the subdorsal and lateral lines whitish.
2. Ground colour pale greenish-buff with all the markings clearer and of a richer rose colour; the subdorsal and lateral lines cream-yellow.
3. Ground colour of clear, light green without any pink, but with a light yellow lateral line.

After the third moult, colour Form 1 becomes much more brilliant and the dorsal and lateral bands of deep pink strongly contrast with the light green sides, and the ventral surface and claspers are green. When fully-grown this Form becomes entirely pinkish-purple with a paler pink lateral band.

Form 3 becomes a dull, pinkish colour when fully-grown. A specimen reared from an egg from Glengarriff, Co. Cork, a female, was of Form 1, but the pinkish-purple markings were faint, as were the lateral yellow lines.

The last three segments are flattened and the whole ventral surface is flattened with a basal ridge extending around the larva, concealing the legs. When at rest the larva appears to be legless. On the dorsal surface of the tenth segment there is a transverse honey gland. The spiracles are inconspicuous, being located in the central groove of each segment. They are white with a black outline.

The surface of the larva is covered with minute, star-like processes from the centre of which springs a serrated spine. The largest spines occur on the dorsal surface as well as on the sides, where they are placed in two oblique patches on each segment.

The larvae of the spring brood feed off the flower-buds of holly, *Ilex aquifolium*, whilst those of the autumn brood feed on the flower-buds of ivy, *Hedera helix*.

The larval stage lasts about 26 days.

PUPA (Fig. 28C)

Stout and 'dumpy' in shape, this pupa is about 8.5 mm in length and is without any acute projections. The metathorax is constricted and the abdomen swollen, giving a waisted appearance, allowing the silken girdle to hold the pupa firmly. The ground colour of the thorax and wing cases is tawny-buff, but the abdomen has a pinkish tinge. All parts of the pupa are liberally sprinkled with marks and spots of a scorched brown colour. These are more particularly evident as an interrupted mid-dorsal line from the head to the termination of the abdomen and on the margins of the thoracic nota, with a pair of darker blotches on the metanotum and a lateral series of blotches on the abdomen which increase in size towards the hinder end. The surface of the whole pupa, with the exception of the wing cases, is moderately shiny, but careful examination of the pupa with a x10 lens or microscope reveals that all surfaces are covered with short brown hairs, each arising from a minute protuberance. A cremaster is present as a circlet of club-shaped hooks fixed to a silken pad at the anal segment. The pupae produced from spring butterflies are attached to holly leaves, the spines of these forming some protection as they curl around the pupa. The pupal stage in the summer brood is about 18 days long, but in the autumn brood the pupae overwinter.

FAMILY NYMPHALIDAE

This is the largest butterfly family and it is distributed worldwide. They are characterized by the adults possessing four walking legs only, the generally spiny larvae, and the pupae which hang suspended by a cremaster without the aid of a silken girdle. Members of three sub-families are present in the Irish fauna: the NYMPHALINAE, ARGYNNINAE, and the MELITAEINAE. Some authorities, however, consider the "Browns" to be included as the sub-family SATYRINAE. In this account we treat them as a distinct family, the SATYRIDAE.

Fig. 29   Family Nymphalidae. Sub-family Nymphalinae. Peacock, *Inachis io*. Usually large in size, brilliant colouration on upper surface, sombre on underside.

Fig. 30   Family Nymphalidae. Sub-family Argynninae. (Fritillaries); upper surface fulvous orange-brown, chequered with black. Silver-washed Fritillary, *Argynnis paphia*.

SUB-FAMILY: NYMPHALINAE

SMALL TORTOISESHELL

Aglais urticae (Linnaeus, 1758)

The Small Tortoiseshell is one of Ireland's most widely distributed butterflies. The author has observed upwards of two hundred specimens hibernating in one stone-built cottage in southwest Co. Cork! There are two generations annually—one in which the adults emerge in June and which lay their eggs immediately, producing adults in August and September. It is this brood which hibernates, and they are seen prospecting for hibernation locations as they flutter along the eaves of houses and enter open windows—especially those of upper stories. In buildings they hide very effectively and this is often at the top of curtain folds. They are rarely disturbed! In stone cottages, however, they are subject to predation during hibernation from wrens, bats, and spiders.

The Small Tortoiseshell butterfly is an avid nectar feeder and is often seen on garden plants such as *Buddleia*, Michaelmas daisies and *Sedum*. It is always a delight to watch!

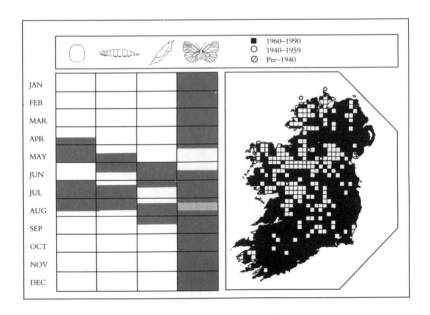

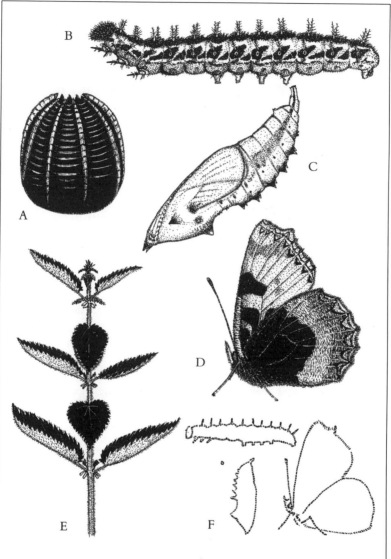

Fig. 31

Small Tortoiseshell: A - Egg (ht. 1mm); B - Larva (L 22mm);
C - Pupa (L 21mm); D - Adult, side-view (wing-span m. 50mm,
f. 56mm); E - Food plant: Stinging nettle, *Urtica dioica*;
F - Life Size

ADULT (Fig. 31D, Plate II H)

When measured across outstretched wings, the male is about 50 mm and the female 56 mm. The sexes are similar except for size.

Like the Red Admiral and the Peacock the wings are scalloped at the edges with a large conical projection on each wing. The ground colour is a tawny orange-red. The margins are broad and black with a row of blue lunules, about three on the forewing and seven on the hindwing. Along the front margin there is a series of rectangular marks. Commencing at the base these are: tawny, black, yellowish cream, black, yellowish-cream, black, white, and black. Towards the centre of the hind margin is an oblong, black mark with a small patch of yellow and two small black spots in the centre of the tawny-orange area. The basal half of the hindwing is black and covered with long fine hairs.

On the underside, the wings have a somewhat similar pattern, but the ground colour is a light yellowish-brown and the black markings of the top surface are replaced by dark brown. The two small spots on the forewings, however, are absent from the underside.

EGG (Fig. 31A)

The eggs are laid in clusters as the female sits on a terminal shoot of stinging nettle, *Urtica dioica,* and bends her abdomen so that they are placed underneath a young leaf. The eggs are globular and oval, with the base larger than the apex. Mating takes place after hibernation and the total number of eggs laid is thought to be about 1000. In size they are about 1 mm in height and the nine longitudinal keels are white and fluted, being largest at the apex, where they project over the micropylar pit. The keels disappear towards the base. A series of transverse ribs extends between the keels.

In colour the eggs are gooseberry-green and shining, but about two days before hatching takes place they become yellowish. The egg stage generally lasts from 8 to 10 days.

LARVA (Fig. 31B)

After hatching, the larvae remain together partially sheltered by webbing, which they spin over the upper part of the plant. At the fourth moult, however, they become solitary.

The length of the larva is about 22 mm when fully fed and having undergone five moults. They vary considerably in ground colour, some being predominantly yellow, whilst others may be almost wholly black. The head is shining black and is somewhat cleft on the upper surface. It is covered with small, green tubercles, each of which bears a black bristle. There are seven longitudinal rows of pyramidal tubercles on which bristles are borne. The mid-dorsal series extends from the fourth to the eleventh segment. In addition the body is speckled with small, pale tubercles, each bearing a white hair. The dorsal surface is blackish with a dark line of spiracles and the body is yellowish to a greater or lesser degree.

The larval stage lasts about twenty-eight days.

PUPA (Fig. 31C)

This is between 20 and 22 mm in length and hangs suspended from a silk pad by means of cremastral hooks. It is smaller and more slender in form than the pupae of the Peacock and Red Admiral.

The head terminates in a pair of sharp pointed projections, whilst the thorax extends to a central, triangular process before diminishing to the thoracic abdominal junction. On the dorsal surface of the abdomen there are three series of conical protuberances. The proboscis sheath and the wings' sheaths extend almost as far as the fifth abdominal segment.

The colour of the pupa varies tremendously from dull, smoky-brown to various metallic sheens, the most common having a golden lustre.

The pupal stage lasts only about twelve days.

PEACOCK

Inachis io (Linnaeus, 1758)

The thrill of seeing these most beautiful butterflies was first experienced by the author as long ago as 1917 when peeping over a stone wall to see half a dozen of these glorious insects sucking nectar from a patch of thistles—the small boy's wonderment has never left me. They were recognised immediately by their peacock-eye marked upper sides and their black, lace-like undersides.

The Peacock is attracted to many species of flowering plants, but especially to *Buddleia*.

It is fairly well distributed, although not quite so frequent in the North as in the South. It hibernates as an adult, usually in a hollow tree trunk, wood-piles, and similar situations from which it makes an appearance in the first warm sunny days of spring. Often this may be as early as March. It is a fast flyer and continues to be so even when its wings are in tatters after hibernation.

ADULT (Fig. 32D, Plate II J)
Measured across the outstretched wings, the male is about 63 mm and the female about 69 mm. The sexes are similar, except for size. The upper and undersides are extraordinarily dissimilar, so that when the wings are open the colouration is vivid and eye-catching but when closed merge into the shadow of their background.

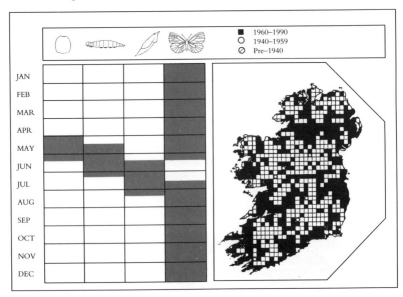

110

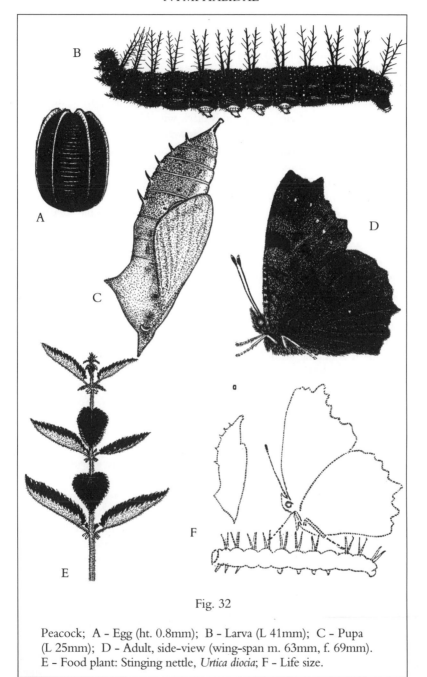

Fig. 32

Peacock; A - Egg (ht. 0.8mm); B - Larva (L 41mm); C - Pupa
(L 25mm); D - Adult, side-view (wing-span m. 63mm, f. 69mm).
E - Food plant: Stinging nettle, *Urtica diocia*; F - Life size.

The ground colour of the upper side is mahogany-red and the characteristic feature of this butterfly is the large, 'peacock eyes' on both the fore and hind-wings. On the forewing, the 'eye' consists of a tawny-red pupil which is encircled by a creamy-yellow near the front margin and by amethyst-lilac on the opposite side, with two similar spots more towards the central area of the wing. Two black patches separated by creamy-yellow arise from the front margin. On the hindwing the pupil is black with blue patches. Around the pupil is a light-grey circle with a black area towards the front margin. The outer margin of all wings is dark grey and there is a conical projection.

. The underside is sombre. A black wavy line divides the wings transversely across the centre. The darker, basal half contains several black bands. The outer half is only slightly lighter with innumerable, black transverse marks, but becomes darker again towards the outer margin—the whole appearance being that of the finest black lace.

EGG (Fig. 32A)
The eggs are laid in piles, several deep, and usually there are several hundred eggs in each mass. They are laid underneath the young leaves of stinging nettle, *Urtica dioica*, in April and May, after the adult has hibernated through the winter.

The egg is small for the size of the adult, being only about 0.8 mm in height. In shape it is oblong with 8 longitudinal ribs originating near the base and enlarging towards the apex where they curl over into the micropyle. The latter is finely pitted. Between the ribs are numerous minute transverse ribs. When newly laid the egg is yellowish-green, turning olive green later. It becomes dark green just before emergence. The larva hatch after about 7–12 days.

LARVA (Fig. 32B)
All the larvae from a batch of eggs hatch simultaneously and they collect together under a web of silk. During the entire larval period they feed and moult gregariously, and the compact mass of black larvae is very conspicuous. When fully grown they are about 41mm in length, although some larvae are recorded at 44mm. Roughly cylindrical in shape and comparatively slender, each segment is barrel-shaped. The first segment is very small. The ground colour of the whole larva is velvety black with numerous black spines which are shiny and sharply pointed and bear many variously sized bristles. The spines occur in six longitudinal series on segments five to eleven, with segments two and three bearing dorsal spines only, and segment four and the anal segment having four spines. There are numerous small, white protuberances from each of which a fine white hair arises.

The claspers are light brown in colour, their bases being more reddish. Peacock larvae are extremely agile, moving about quite rapidly. When

PLATE I

A. Dingy Skipper	G. Small White	N. Green Hairstreak
B. Brimstone *m.*	H. Green-veined White *m.*	(underside)
C. Brimstone *f.*	J. Green-veined White *f.*	O. Brown Hairstreak *m.*
D. Wood White	K. Orange-tip *m.*	P. Brown Hairstreak *f.*
E. Large White *m.*	L. Orange-tip *f.*	Q. Purple Hairstreak *m.*
F. Large White *f.*	M. Green Hairstreak	R. Purple Hairstreak *f.*

PLATE II

A. Small Copper
B. Small Blue *m.*
C. Small Blue *f.*
D. Common Blue *m.*
E. Common Blue *f.*

F. Holly Blue *m.*
G. Holly Blue *f.*
H. Small Tortoiseshell
J. Peacock

K. Pearl Bordered Fritillary
L. Dark Green Fritillary
M. Silver-washed Fritillary *m.*
N. Silver-washed Fritillary *f.*
O. Marsh Fritillary

PLATE III

A. Speckled Wood
B. Gatekeeper *m.*
C. Gatekeeper *f.*
D. Grayling *m.*
E. Grayling *f.*
F. Wall *m.*

G. Wall *f.*
H. Meadow Brown *f.*
J. Meadow Brown *m.*
K. Large Heath
L. Ringlet

M. Small Heath
N. Red Admiral
O. Clouded Yellow *m.*
P. Clouded Yellow *f.*
Q. Painted Lady

PLATE IV

A. Bath White
B. Pale Clouded Yellow
C. Camberwell Beauty

D. American Painted Lady
E. Queen of Spain Fritillary
F. Monarch
G. Large Copper *m.*

H. Large Copper *f.*
J. Heath Fritillary
K. Small Mountain Ringlet

disturbed they elevate the forepart of the body into a hook-shape and when irritated will fall to the ground wriggling violently.

The larval stage lasts about 28 days.

PUPA (Fig. 32C)

About 25 mm in length, the female is a little larger than the male. It hangs vertically downwards by strong cremastral hooks attached to a pad of silk. It has a somewhat elongated appearance. Two pronounced 'horns' diverge from the head and a conspicuous pointed protuberance rises from the centre of the thorax with a pair of smaller ones on each side. Five pairs of backwardly directed spines are borne by the abdomen on the upper surface, which are rosy at the base and black at the tip. Except for the intersegmental membrane, the whole of the pupa is covered with a fine reticulation of black and dark greyish-brown. The cremaster is light buff. There is a wide variation in ground colour from rosy-grey to greenish-yellow, and a certain amount of gilding of variable extent on the head, thorax and wings. The spiracles are lined with black and are relatively conspicuous.

Shortly before emergence, the wing colouration of the adult may be seen. The pupal stage lasts from 12 to 14 days.

PEARL-BORDERED FRITILLARY

Boloria euphrosyne (Linnaeus, 1758))

The Pearl-bordered Fritillary is known as an Irish butterfly only since 1922, when it was discovered in the Burren, Co. Clare by R. A. Phillips, to which region it is apparently confined.

There are, however, two records of the occurrence of this species at some distance from the Burren: an old record which was unaccepted by Baynes for the Foynes/Askeaton area south of Shannon and southwest of Limerick (it is thought now that this record is correct, however, confirmation is awaited); and a 1974 record of one butterfly from near Pallas Green in Co. Tipperary, southeast of Limerick. This later record is now discounted as being an error of identification of a butterfly seen only in flight. When freshly emerged it is a fast

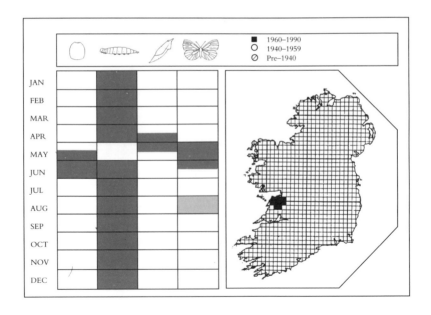

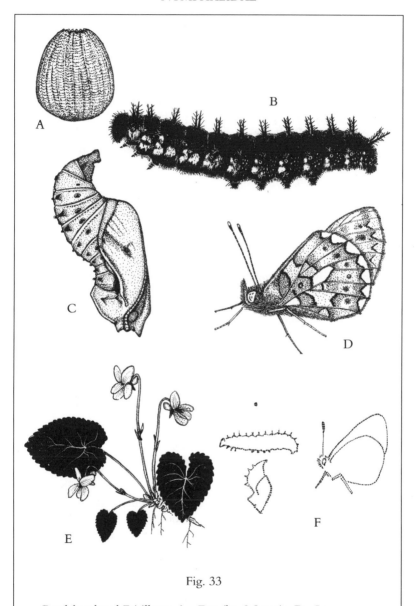

Fig. 33

Pearl-bordered Fritillary: A - Egg (ht. 0.8mm); B - Larva
(L 25mm); C - Pupa (L 14mm); D - Adult, side-view (wing-
span m. 44mm f. 47mm); E - Food plant: Dog violet, *Viola
riviniana;* F - Life size.

flyer and most difficult to keep up with as it is impossible to run quickly over the limestone pavement of the Burren. It is usually on the wing from the middle of May to the middle of June, but this species is very weather dependent.

ADULT (Fig. 33D, Plate II K)

The distance across expanded wings is about 44 mm in the male and about 47 mm in the female. The ground colour is generally described as rich fulvous (similarly with the Dark Green and Silver-washed Fritillaries) but 'orange-tawny' is equally descriptive. The upper side of the wings is spotted and spangled with black and all the veins are black. The bases of the wings are dusky—the hindwings more conspicuously—and dusted with fulvous. Four lunate, transverse marks occur on the forewings within the wing cell and this row of marks continues towards the apex with three further marks. The outer margin of the wings is black which thickens at the termination of the veins. A row of black triangular marks is located just within the outer margin, and a row of small spots further towards the base. Roughly parallel with the row of marks in the cell is a row of four marks, the basal one being lunate, and between this and the outer margin there is a prominent square mark. The hind wings are rather similar.

On the underside, the forewings are much paler and the black marks of the upperside are repeated, but there are some silver spots at the apex, bordered on the inside with reddish-chocolate. The hindwing bears a row of seven silver triangular marks around the outer margin and a large silver mark in the centre. There is a triangular silver mark at the base set in an area of reddish-chocolate. There is a band of similar colouration within the outer silver spots and the central silver mark is set within a band of yellowish-brown.

EGG (FIG. 33A)

This is laid on low-growing plants in the vicinity of, or on, various violet species. It is about 0.8 mm in height and is cream in colour at first, turning yellowish-green, then brown, shortly before emergence. Globular in shape, it tapers towards the apex where there is a concavity. There are longitudinal ridges or keels which vary in number, the average being about twenty-five. Whereas some of the keels run from base to apex, others commence at various points where they diverge and then terminate at the base. Where they meet around the concave micropyle "they form a zig-zag brim of triangular points" (Frohawk, 1924). A pattern of transverse ribbing is present which is clearly seen to extend over the longitudinal ridges. The whole egg is shining and the ridges reflect the light. The length of the egg stage is from 10 to 15 days.

LARVA (FIG. 33B)

On hatching (about the end of May), the young larvae (then less than 1.5 mm in length) immediately commence to feed very actively on the new shoots of common dog violet, *Viola riviniana*, during the daytime. They continue thus until the end of the third moult, when they are just over 10mm in length. Their appearance is now spiny, fat and very black. Hibernation takes place immediately, often within a dry, curled-up leaf or two of the Dog violet. The larvae remain motionless, contracting in length to about 6.3 mm until about the middle of the following March, when they recommence to feed. A rapid increase in size again takes place, but pupation varies very much according to temperature. The fully grown larvae measure up to 25.4 mm in length and are cylindrical in shape, except for a slight attenuation towards the head.

The ground colour on the upper surface is black and smokey-brown underneath.

PUPA (Fig. 33C)

About 14 mm in length, it hangs from a pad of silk by cremastral hooks. It has a rather stumpy appearance. The head is broad with two blunt horns pointing forwards. The thorax has a high angular keel and the wing cases are prominent, pointed at the base and extending well below the ventral surface of the arched abdomen. Running along the length of the upper surface are two rows of conical projections which are inconspicuous and blunt on the thorax, but on the third abdominal segment they are large. They then decrease in size towards the hinder end, and those on the sixth and seventh segments are joined.

The general ground colour is light grey and pinkish on the upper surface, which is covered with fine, reddish-brown, reticulated pencilling. The dorsal projections are reddish, and where the wing veins show through there are double rows of white spots. In captivity it is recorded by the author that nine days only are spent in the pupal stage.

DARK GREEN FRITILLARY

Argynnis aglaja (Linnaeus, 1758)

This large, rapid-flying fritillary is usually found on rough hillsides, cliffs and in open spaces near the sea. The larval food plant is common dog violet, *Viola riviniana*, (however marsh violet, *V. palustris* is often used as an alternative) so that the situations described above require to have this species growing fairly abundantly. This usually occurs even in exposed places, but where the violet plants can grow with some protection amongst other vegetation. This butterfly may be seen closely enough to be identified with its convex outer margin of the forewings, whilst it sucks nectar from the blossoms of thistles to which it is also greatly attracted. It has a fairly wide distribution and is usually plentiful where it occurs.

The Dark Green Fritillary overwinters as a newly emerged larva and it is single-brooded.

ADULT (Fig. 34D, Plate II L)
This butterfly measures about 63 mm (male) and 69 mm (female) across the outstretched wings. The ground colour is a rich orange-brown and this is chequered, barred and spotted with velvety black. Except for shape,

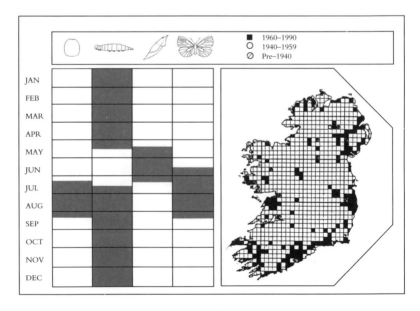

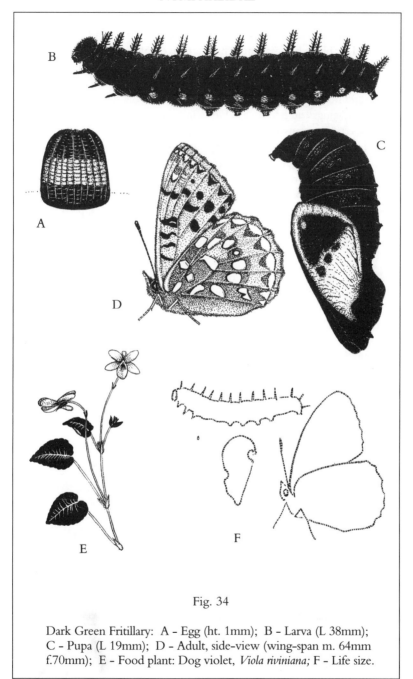

Fig. 34

Dark Green Fritillary: A - Egg (ht. 1mm); B - Larva (L 38mm);
C - Pupa (L 19mm); D - Adult, side-view (wing-span m. 64mm
f.70mm); E - Food plant: Dog violet, *Viola riviniana;* F - Life size.

fore- and hindwings are similar in colour and patterning. The outer margins are black, divided by a thin yellowish line, and a series of yellowish lunules bordered by black lie adjacent. There are seven of these on each wing.

In the female, the apical area of the forewing is yellowish and there may also be a lighter area in the centre of the hindwing.

Inwards from the lunules, in both sexes, there is a transverse row of spots, six on the forewings and five on the hindwings, of which the third spot is much the smallest. The transverse band of chequered spots across the centre of the wings joins a row of figure-like marks adjacent to the front margin towards the base. On the underside, the black markings on the forewings are not unlike that of the upper surface, but the apical area is greenish and a number of the lunules near the apex are silvery. The underside of the hindwings, however, is very different. The basal and anal area of the wings is dark apple-green with thirteen large, silvery spots. The outer area is tinged with seven lunate, silvery spots edged with dark green on the inside, whilst the margin is yellow.

EGG (Fig. 34A)

This is about 1 mm in height and rounded-conical in form. It is flat at the base and slightly concave at the top, resembling a lobster pot. There are about 20 longitudinal ridges, none of which reach entirely to the base and of which only about half commence at the apex of the egg, the others starting from about three-quarters to half-way down. There are about 20 lateral ribs which are more pronounced near the top. When first laid, the egg is pale yellow but then it turns yellowish-brown in colour. After a few days the upper and basal thirds become lilac coloured, whilst the central area becomes greenish-yellow. It gradually darkens until just before hatching, when it is dark brown on top and the remainder pearl grey. This stage lasts about 17 days.

LARVA (Fig. 34B)

When fully grown, after five moults, it is about 38 mm in length. One larva reared from West Cork measured 44mm. The ground colour is a shining purplish grey, thickly mixed with velvety-black. The grey colour occurs mostly between the segments and along the lower part of the sides. There is a yellow, mid-dorsal stripe in the centre of which is a black line. A series of bright-red spots joined by a fine yellow line occurs towards the base of the sides. The black head is shiny and hairy and the body bears a number of large black branched spines. On the thoracic segments there are two rows on each side, and three rows on the abdominal segments.

The newly hatched larvae immediately crawl down amongst the roots of the violet plant and hibernate without feeding, except on the egg shell.

PUPA (Fig. 34C)

The pupa is about 19 mm in length but it is strongly arched, the last segments projecting at right angles to the body bringing them close to the wing cases. It is thick and robust also, being about 8.5 mm in width, and hangs by the cremaster attached to a silken pad. It is usually screened by a few leaves drawn together by silk threads. The ground colour is yellowish or brownish, but is heavily blotched with dark brown or black. The spiracles are conspicuously black and each abdominal segment is marked with purple. There is a fine dark purplish reticulation over the wing cases and legs, and the whole surface is shining, generally with a burnt appearance. It is extremely agile and if disturbed will wriggle and twist with great rapidity.

The pupal stage lasts for about 28 days.

SILVER-WASHED FRITILLARY

Argynnis paphia (Linnaeus, 1758)

This large and handsome butterfly is about the same size as the Dark Green Fritillary. It can be easily identified from the latter species (when sucking nectar from thistle and bramble flowers) by the more inwardly sloping and concave outer margin of the forewings.

It has a general distribution throughout Ireland and is associated with old, broad-leaved woodland, appearing not to stray far away from such locations even when they are not extensive. This compares with the Dark Green species which frequents grassy hillsides.

Abroad, the Silver-washed has an extensive distribution throughout Europe and temperate Asia as far as Korea and Japan.

ADULT (Fig. 35D, Plate II M,N)
At about 72 mm across the outstretched wings in the male, and about 76 mm in the female, this is Ireland's largest resident butterfly. The sexes are easily identified—the male has a ground colour of bright, fulvous orange on the upper surface with distinct, darker markings, making the insect very conspicuous in flight when freshly emerged; the female is much paler with less distinct markings. Its flight is strong and rapid, alternating between a metre or so from

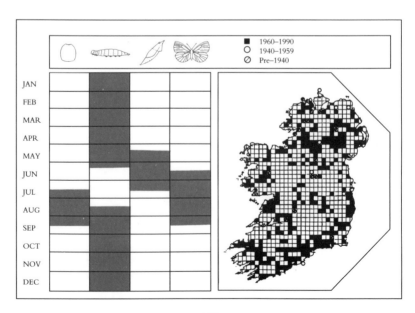

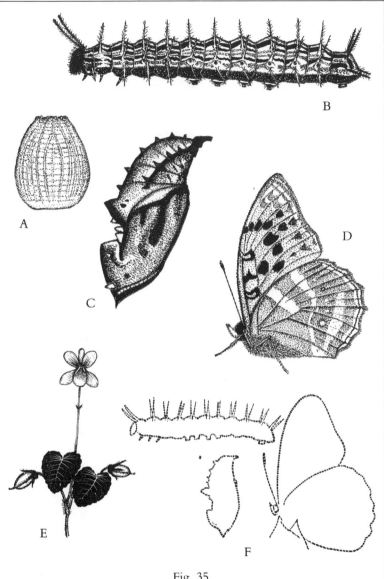

Fig. 35

Silver-washed Fritillary: A - Egg (ht. 1mm); B - Larva
(L 38mm); C - Pupa (L 22mm); D - Adult, side-view (wing-
span m. 72mm, f. 76mm); E - Food plant: Dog violet, *Viola
riviniana;* F - Life size.

the ground and the tops of the highest oaks. Both fore- and hind-wings are heavily spotted and barred with black or purplish-black with the spots less prominent around the apex. The wing veins in the centre are black due to the presence of androconial scales. The outer margins of fore- and hindwings are scalloped. The position of the black spots is shown in the illustration. On the underside of the forewing, apart from the green apex, the ground colour is also fulvous orange, and the spots similar to those of the upper surface except that they are fainter and smaller. The ground colour of the hindwing is bronze-green across which 4 wavy, but generally wedge-shaped bars of whitish-silver, extend from the costal margin to the anal angle.

Along the outer margin a number of green spots are enclosed by the outer silver band, whilst variable areas of the hinder parts of the wing are shot with amethyst and sometimes other colours.

EGG (Fig. 35A)

The egg is usually laid in a crevice in the bark of a tree a couple of metres above the ground. Both oak and pine have been recorded, often in a situation where the common dog violet, *Viola riviniana*, is abundant. The egg is about 1mm in height which is small for Ireland's largest butterfly, and is higher than it is wide, narrowing towards the top where the micropyle is situated within a crenelated circlet. There are about 25 longitudinal ridges, of which about 12 run the full length of the egg, and the remainder arise at various points. The base of the egg is flattened and is fixed in position.

In captivity the eggs may be laid on cotton netting, the female passing her ovipositor through the mesh so that the eggs are laid on the 'outside'. In colour the egg is a light greenish-yellow with a tinge of light brown. Later the egg becomes light-brownish, with the top a leaden-grey colour. (This is the head of the larva when it starts to bite its way out of the egg.)

The egg stage lasts about 14 days.

LARVA (Fig. 35B)

This is one of the most remarkable life histories of all the Irish butterflies. When the young larva hatches it is only just over 2 mm in length. It hibernates immediately and remains in this state for about eight months. Thus, hatching in early August, it does not commence to feed until the beginning of the following April.

The egg is laid several metres from its food plant, common dog violet, *Viola riviniana*, usually on the bark of an oak or other tree a metre or so above the ground. Thus the main task of the young larva is to find its way to this one species. Death would follow its inability to do so.

In captivity the larva remains motionless for weeks or months on end but, if disturbed, drops to the ground and crawls away quickly to find another place of shelter. When reaching a plant of common dog violet (in the spring), it feeds voraciously during the day on the young shoots, making its way quickly from plant to plant. When almost full-grown it can consume a large leaf in less than two minutes! It is then about 38 mm in length. Although generally cylindrical, the larva tapers somewhat towards the head and less so at the hinder end.

Ground colour is dark purplish-brown with yellow-brown streaking and blotching. A mid-dorsal, yellowish-brown double stripe runs the whole length of the larva, with a pattern of purplish-black speckling and blotching on a yellowish-brown background below.

There are sixty-two conspicuous yellowish-brown bristled spines, with the first pair on the first segment differing from the remainder, but otherwise uniformly thick, projecting forwards and upwards and with blunt tips. There are two pairs on the second segment, four on the third as well as on the last segment, and six on the remainder. The head is shining black with a few buff streaks on top and covered with bristles.

The length of the larval stage is about 10 months.

PUPA (Fig. 35C)

The pupa, which is about 22 mm in length, hangs suspended from a pad of silk attached to the cremastral hooks. Frohawk wrote that it 'greatly resembles a withered brown, curled-up leaf with sparkling drops of dew attached to it'.

At the head, there are two diverging horns and, viewed from above, the metathorax is conspicuously wide, but gradually decreases in width to the cremaster. Viewed from the side, the thorax is prominently keeled and there is a pronounced hump on the first abdominal segment. There are two series of pointed projections, the first five pairs of which possess a metallic lustre of extraordinary brilliance.

The ground colour of the pupa is pale buff, finely reticulated with dark brown. There are also brown bands which give the effect of veins of a leaf.

The pupal stage lasts for about 18 days.

MARSH FRITILLARY

Eurodryas aurinia (Rottemburg, 1775)

The Marsh Fritillary occurs in damp meadows and on hillsides where devil's bit scabious, *Succisa pratensis*, grows abundantly. It is usually present in colonies, aided by the behaviour of the larvae which feed gregariously in a web. The colony, however, moves about from time to time. Full-grown larvae have been found in honeysuckle in West Cork. This butterfly is single-brooded and the winter is spent as a larva within the web. It is fairly well distributed in Ireland, although local (Lavery, in press).

ADULT (Fig. 36D, Plate II O)
This butterfly measures about 42 mm (male) and about 48 mm (female) across the outstretched wings. The ground colour is reddish-orange inclined to carmine, with the veins marked with black. On all wings there is a transverse band of yellowish-cream or nearly white, margined with black, and divided into spots by the veins. There is a large black basal area on the hind wing and a smaller one on the forewing. The margins are black, and these carry an outer series of small cream bars and an inner of crescent-shaped spots.

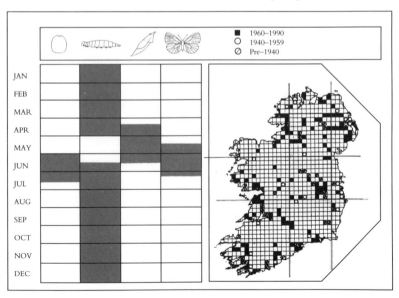

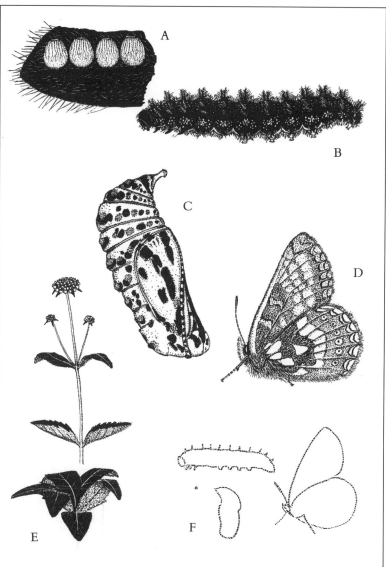

Fig. 36

Marsh Fritillary: A - Egg (ht. 0.8mm) B - Larva (L 30mm);
C - Pupa (L 14.8mm); D - Adult, side-view (wing-span m.42mm,
f.48mm); E - Food plant: Devil's bit scabious, *Succisa pratensis*;
F - Life size.

Both sexes are similar except for size. On the underside the forewing is pale fuscous, with the patterning of the upper side showing through in a rather suffused manner. On the hindwing there is no black and the markings are more definite and show the upper side patterning, but there are additional cream-coloured marks at the base and a row of six black-pupilled white marks, corresponding with black spots on the upper surface. Irish Marsh Fritillaries have in the past been referred to as subspecies *hibernica* (Birchall); however it is now accepted that only the nominate subspecies occurs in Ireland.

EGG (Fig. 36A)

The eggs are laid in large clusters, usually several hundred in number, and deposited on the underside of a leaf of the food plant. Frohawk writes of a 'heaped-up batch', but those laid in the rearing cages of the author were arranged as a flat plate. The egg is about 0.8 mm in height and approximately spherical in shape, but is widest rather nearer the base than the middle line and, whilst the base is rounded, the top is flattened and slightly concave. About 20 ribs run longitudinally, prominent where they originate at the apex of the egg, then branching at about the half-way mark and then disappearing, so that the basal one-third is smooth.

At first the egg is lemon-yellow with a varnished appearance; but after a few days, it assumes a rather more brownish colour. Then, on about the eighth day it becomes a dark greyish-brown and leaden thereafter. Finally, the dark head of the embryo larva can be seen through the shell. Frohawk gives the length of the egg stage as 20 days, but a batch of eggs laid in West Cork took over a month to hatch.

LARVA (Fig. 36B)

Soon after emergence, the batch of young larvae crowd together on a leaf of devil's bit scabious and spin a web. They then pull a few leaves together with silk threads, making a shelter within which they feed. From time to time they will leave the shelter and take up another situation, which they deal with in the same way. Towards the end of August they spin a compact web in which hibernation takes place. On sunny days they leave the hibernaculum, but retreat inside when the sun disappears.

The fully grown larva reaches a length of about 30mm by the end of April. The upper surface is velvety black and the lower surface is brownish with a greyish-white stripe. This consists of a series of white spots and a flower-like pattern surrounding the spiracle on each segment. The body tapers slightly at each end. The velvety-black head bears a number of bristles and there are longitudinal rows of black spines, all bearing bristles along the length of the body. There are seven series in all—one in the mid-dorsal line; two just below the dorsal surface and one immediately below the spiracles.

They are very agile, and when disturbed, roll into a ball but, as quickly, will unroll and crawl rapidly away.

The winter is passed as a half or three-quarters grown larva (fourth instar larva). After 6 months the fully grown larva measures *c.* 28 mm in length.

PUPA (Fig. 36C)

The pupa measures up to about 14.8 mm in length. The head end is blunt and rounded, whilst the abdomen curves ventrally. The pupa is held in this position by the cremaster being firmly fixed to a silken pad. The ground colour is greyish-white, and the wing cases are paler but blotched with lilac-grey. The abdomen is yellowish. Except for the abdomen, the pupa is spotted and marked with black, whilst the larval tubercles become orange knobs. Whilst the spiracles are inconspicuous, they are set within the black marks. The antennal covers are banded with black and orange.

The pupal stage lasts about fifteen days.

FAMILY SATYRIDAE

This family is sometimes considered to be a sub-family of the NYMPH-ALIDAE. However, the "Browns", as they are sometimes called, differ from Nymphalids in not being so brilliantly coloured on the upper side, being abundantly decorated with eye-like markings and most species seldom rest with their wings outspread. Additionally, characteristic larvae are long, slender, attenuated; the tail region is forked, and the body usually longitudinally striped in brown and green. In some cases the pupae are fixed, suspended by means of a cremaster and sometimes with a girdle; in others, the pupa lies on the ground.

The larval food plants are invariably species of grass GRAMINEAE, with the exception (in Irish Satyridae) that the Large Heath larvae feed on a species of sedge, CYPERACEAE.

SPECKLED WOOD

Pararge aegeria subspecies *tircis* (Godart, 1821)

This is generally a butterfly of shady situations, such as the edges of woodland, forest paths and especially hedges. It flies continually from sunlit areas to shady spots and possesses strong territorial instincts, often buffeting other butterflies that trespass. However, in some localities it flourishes remote from woodland areas. It first appears in April, probably having emerged from overwintering larvae. Those adults seen in late May are usually from overwintering larvae. Hereafter there is a second brood, with great variation in emergence times. The broods tend to overlap, so that this species is often on the wing from mid–April until the middle of October and sometimes later. It is widely distributed and abundant. The larval food plants are various grass species: *Agropyron repens* and *Dactylis glomerata* being conspicuous among these.

ADULT (Fig. 38D, Plate III A)
This butterfly measures about 47 mm (male) and 50 mm (female) across the outstretched wings. The upper side is very dark brown—dappled with creamy-yellow patches, some of which are suffused with brown scales. On the forewings, near the apex, is a black eye-spot set in a creamy patch and with a

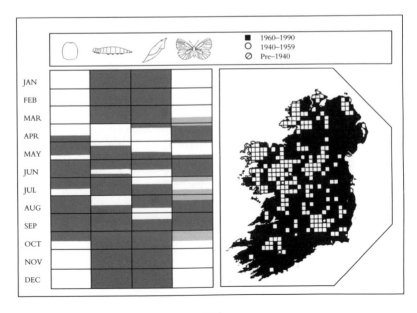

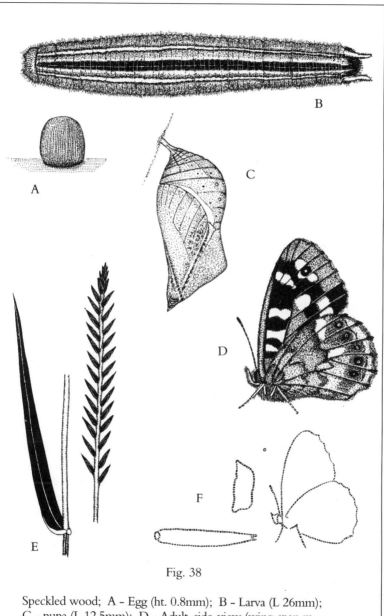

Fig. 38

Speckled wood; A - Egg (ht. 0.8mm); B - Larva (L 26mm);
C - pupa (L 12.5mm); D - Adult, side-view (wing-span m.
47mm. f.50mm): E - Food plant: Couch grass *Agropyron repens*;
F - Life size.

white pupil. On the hindwings there are three such eye-spots near the outer edge. Early specimens have larger cream spots than later ones.

In the male there is an oblique band of androconial scales in the centre of the forewings, which is rather more easily seen if the butterfly is held against the light. The male is smaller than the female. In the latter, however, the wings are somewhat rounder and the creamy-yellow patches are usually larger.

EGG (Fig. 38A)

The eggs are laid singly on the blades of various grass species, especially couch *Agropyron repens*, and cock's foot, *Dactylis glomerata*. Like all the Irish satyrids, the egg is more or less spheroidal, but is slightly wider near the base and is somewhat flattened, as is the apex. It measures about 0.80mm in height and is greenish-yellow in colour, and the semi-translucence gives it a pearl-like appearance. A close examination with a lens shows the whole surface to be finely reticulated, brought about by longitudinal ridges and fine, transverse ribbing. About 10 days are spent in the egg stage and, shortly before hatching, the dark coloured head of the embryo larva can be seen near the top of the egg.

LARVA (Fig. 38B)

On hatching, the young larva is yellow and the large head is black and globular. After undergoing 3 moults it becomes fully grown, measuring from 25-29 mm. In shape it is slender, being widest at about the second abdominal segment and decreasing towards the head and the anal segment. The prominent head is large and bilobed at the crown. Each lobe is pyramidal and projects well above the first thoracic segment. In colour, the head is bright green and covered with grey hair, each hair being borne on a small tubercle. The eye-spots are brown. The thoracic segments are each divided into 4, and the abdominal segments into 6 sub-divisions. The first sub-division in each case is generally the widest. The general body colour is 'grass-green', but striped longitudinally as follows. There is a conspicuous dark green stripe running the length of the back, which narrows to the front and behind, and generally proportionate to the width of the segments. On each side of this stripe is one of greenish-yellow which accentuates it. Below, on each side, is another yellow line bordered by a narrow, dark green stripe. The yellow spiracles are small, and below them is another (but narrower and fainter) yellowish stripe bordered by darker green.

The ventral surface is 'clear translucent green'. The whole body is covered with white tubercles, each bearing a grey hair. The anal segment extends as a flap over the claspers, and on each side there is a hairy white horn-shaped projection. The length of the larval stage is very variable from about 3 to 4 weeks in the summer brood to as long as 7 months in the case of spring-emerging adults.

PUPA (Fig. 38C)

Immediately before pupation, the longitudinal stripes on the larva disappear and a clear green is assumed. Spinning a small, but thick, silken pad on a blade of grass, it then hangs downwards from the pad held by the anal claspers. The body takes up almost a complete loop and the head is held against the ninth segment, not quite touching the claspers. The pupa measures between 12-13 mm in length and just about half this in width at its widest, which is the central part of the abdomen. In general appearance it is very stout, and is held away from the leaf blade by the strongly stalked cremaster. The head is bilobed, being terminated by two widely spaced 'horns'. The upper surface of the thorax is conspicuously humped, whilst the base of the wing region projects outwards as a ridge. The abdomen is rounded, wide and thick, and tapers abruptly to the stalk of the cremaster, which is longitudinally grooved on the upper surface. The numerous cremastral hooks are brown and are provided with long stalks.

There is some variation in colour. At first the pupae are translucent, brilliant green and finely mottled, and, whilst some remain thus others darken to a light olive-brown. With much variation in intensity, the tips of the 'horns' are brown, as is the veination of the wings, the base of the wings (in the pupa this is the upper margin), where it is edged by a white stripe and four longitudinal bands on each side of the abdomen.

The wing region is usually lighter in hue, sometimes whitish. The spiracles are small and light red in colour.

On the upper surface of the abdomen (on segments 2 to 6 inclusive) there are two rows of white shiny tubercles. There is a limited amount of sideways movement of the last five abdominal segments.

This stage lasts about 4 weeks, or 6 months or so in the case of overwintering.

WALL BROWN

Lasiommata megera (Linnaeus, 1767)

Known also simply as the 'Wall', this is a sun-loving butterfly active only in bright sunlight. It is, then, generally to be seen resting with wings outstretched on stones, bare paths and brick walls—hence its name. On being disturbed it flits around for short distances, then selects another such resting place, keeping more or less to a restricted territory. It usually occurs in open country.

The Wall Brown is usually double-brooded, but in favourable summers there may be three broods. The adults of the first brood appear in May and June and those of the second in July and August. The winter is passed as young larvae feeding from time to time as the weather allows. It is widely distributed and often abundant throughout Ireland.

ADULT (Fig. 39D, Plate III F,G)
Measuring about 44 mm (male) and 46 mm (female) across, the outstretched wings are bright fulvous (reddish-yellow or dull, reddish-brown) with the veins, margins and transverse markings blackish-brown. The upper side of the forewings, near the apex, is marked with a black spot with a white pupil. The hindwings have four similar spots near the outer edge, except that the fourth spot lacks a pupil.

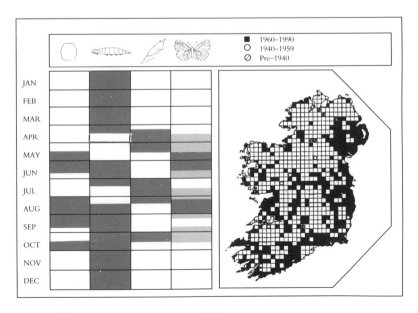

136

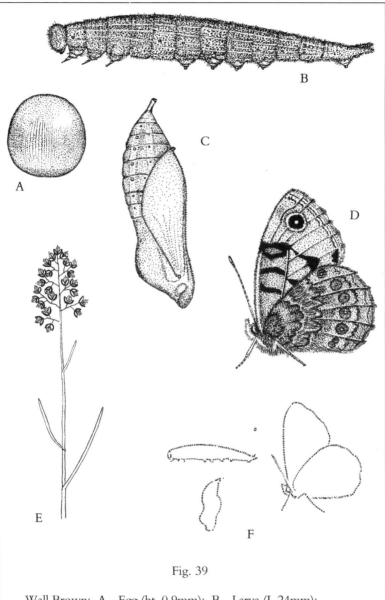

Fig. 39

Wall Brown: A - Egg (ht. 0.9mm); B - Larva (L 24mm);
C - Pupa (L 16mm); D - Adult, side-view (wing-span m. 44mm,
f. 46mm); E - Food plant: Annual meadow grass, *Poa annua*;
F - Life size.

In the male only, there is an easily observed sexual bar in the centre of the forewing. In both sexes the underside of the forewing is paler and the margins are somewhat greyer. The hindwings are grey with brown marks and transverse dark lines. Towards the outer margin there are six eye-spots; the innermost one is small, but double. The wings of the female are wider, due to the front margin being more convex, and the central transverse marks are generally narrower and more distinct.

EGG (Fig. 39A)

The egg is laid singly on a blade of grass. It is spheroidal in shape, about 0.9 mm in height, and large compared with the size of the adult butterfly. It is only slightly flattened at top and bottom, widest near the base, and is only a little longer than it is wide. It is pale yellowish-green, and the whole surface is covered with a very fine reticulation which, even with a x10 lens, only resolves itself into longitudinal ridges over the middle one-third or so of the egg surface. Shortly before the young larva emerges the egg becomes opaque and the long, black hairs of the embryo can be seen as dark streaks through the shell.

The egg stage lasts about 10 days.

LARVA (Fig. 39B)

When fully grown in spring it reaches a length of about 24 mm. It is widest at the middle segments but the decrease in size of the hindmost segments is most marked. The head, which is larger than the first thoracic segment, is bright apple green, whilst the body is slightly darker with a rather bluish, velvety appearance. There is a dark green, median-dorsal, longitudinal line, which is edged with an indistinct, pale, fine stripe. On each side are three longitudinal whitish lines, the central one of which is faint and in the lowest of which are situated the spiracles, which are light orange in colour. Below the spiracular line is a more distinct white line edged with dark green. The anal 'points' are also dark green. The whole body is beset with white warts, from each of which arises a fine, pale-coloured hair, giving the caterpillar a velvety sheen. It moves only very slowly. The food plants consist of several grasses, but *Poa annua* and *Dactylis glomerata* appeared to be preferred. The larval stage of the first brood lasts about 31 days, but that of the over-wintering brood is approximately nine months. Feeding takes place mostly at night.

PUPA (Fig. 39C)

The length averages a little short of 16 mm, and it hangs vertically from a grass blade, where the slender cremaster is hooked onto a silken pad. In shape it is more slender in comparison to its length than other satyrids. The head is wide with a pair of pyramidal projections. The thorax is arched and keeled, whilst the wing cases project from the lower surface of the abdomen. The abdomen is slightly arched and the cremaster is stalked. The ground colour is a bright apple-green, but two rows of tubercles on the upper surface of the abdomen, the crest of the thorax and the angles at the bases of the wing-cases, are white ringed with yellow. Sometimes the pupa is very dark, nearly blackish, with the 'points' white or yellow. The pupal stage lasts about two weeks.

GRAYLING

Hipparchia semele subspecies *hibernica* Howarth, 1971

The Grayling is an inconspicuous, although fairly large, butterfly. It is never seen with outstretched wings. It sucks the nectar of dry heathland flowers such as thyme and heather. This is the only time it can be observed, otherwise it is only seen as it flies up from only a few feet from the place where one is standing and then flutters rather strongly, seemingly carried along by the breeze, to settle within a short distance and then, just as suddenly, disappears. An extremely cautious approach may enable one to observe the butterfly resting with the hindwings covering the forewings; thus hiding the tawny-coloured base. Instead of the wings standing upright, they are seen to be bent over, almost parallel with the rocky or heathy ground on which it has settled. It is also thought that it comes to rest in relation to the position of the sun in order to minimize shadow. The pair of eye-marks on each forewing are also out-of-sight, so that this butterfly relies first on its background colouration for safety from predation and secondly, and perhaps to a much lesser degree, on the small eye-marks on the underside of the forewings. These are 'cocked' only momentarily before escape by flight.

Although there are many inland localities for the Grayling, it is perhaps best known as a coastal species especially common in dry, rocky or sandy situations.

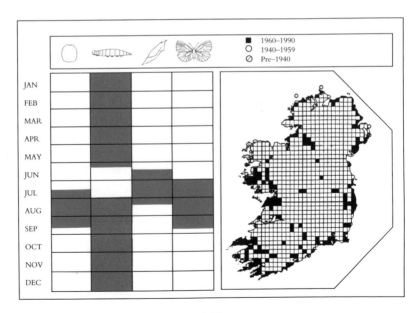

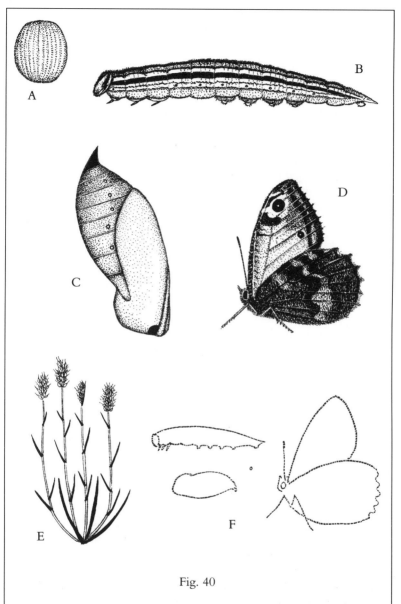

Fig. 40

Grayling: A - Egg (ht. 0.8mm); B - Larva (L 28-31mm);
C - Pupa (L 15-17mm) D - Adult, side-view (wing-span m.
56mm, f. 61mm); E - Food plant: Early hair grass, *Aira praecox*;
F - Life size.

SATYRIDAE

ADULT (Fig. 40D, Plate III D,E)

The outstretched wings of this butterfly measure about 56 mm (male) and 61 mm (female). The upper surface is brown with blackish-brown suffusions, especially in the male, where the creamy or rusty-cream transverse band is almost obliterated. In this band, two white-pupilled, black eye-marks are generally present, although the white pupil may be absent from the lower one. In the hindwings there is a rusty band near the outer brown margin and a small eye-spot is located in it near the anal angle, in which there also may appear a white pupil. On the underside, the upper wings have the inner-half rusty and the outer-half cream, with two eye-spots usually distinct. The hindwings are greyish, banded, and mottled with black, brown and dark-grey streaks. Sub-species *clarensis* (de Lattin), 1952, occurs in the Burren region of Co. Clare and Co. Galway, it is much paler and of a greyer hue than subspecies *hibernica* and in general has the appearance of being somewhat faded or 'washed-out'.

EGG (Fig. 40A)

The egg is laid singly on a blade of grass, although in captivity a number of eggs were laid scattered over the floor of the rearing container. It is spheroidal in shape, but flattened at the top and bottom. In height it is about 0.8mm and is somewhat less in width. There are about 28 irregular longitudinal ridges which unite in a reticulate pattern on the summit, which is slightly concave, and the micropyle shows a number of fine punctures. The colour is milky-white, but before hatching, this changes to a pale lilac-grey. The egg stage lasts about 17 days.

LARVA (Fig. 40B)

When fully grown the larva measures from about 28 mm to 31 mm in length. The body diminishes in size towards the head, which is much smaller than the first segment, whilst tapering much more gradually to the rear. The anal segment bears a pair of horn-like processes. The general body-colour is pale yellow, and there are longitudinal stripes which are broadest in the middle segments. The mid-dorsal stripe is olive-brown edged with brownish-white. In the sub-dorsal region there is firstly a stripe consisting of a yellowish-brown, narrow line and then a somewhat wider second stripe of the mottled ground colour, with a pale edge above and white below. Then a third, dark grey-brown stripe edged above with black. The stripe in which the black spiracles are situated is pale ochreous-brown, edged on each side with brownish-white. The body stripes are continued onto the brown head, but in a darker shade.

The larva feeds on a variety of grass species, including *Agropyron repens*; *Deschampsia caespitosa*; *Aira praecox*; and *Festuca glauca*. It feeds only at night. The winter is passed as a small larva just after the second moult.

PUPA (Fig. 40C)

It varies in length from 15 to 17 mm and in colour from a rich chestnut to dark brown, with the wings and limbs a rich amber. There are no markings, and the cremaster is without hooks. Pupation takes place just below ground level in a loose cocoon made of soil particles bound together with silk, giving a smooth surface to the inside wall. The pupa is not attached in any way and could be mistaken by the inexpert for the pupa of a moth. In shape the rounded head is prominent, whilst the metathorax and first abdominal segment are 'waisted'. The abdomen is largest at the third segment. The spiracles are prominent and the thoracic spiracle bears an 'ear-like ridge' which is black. The pupal stage lasts for about one month.

GATEKEEPER

Pyronia tithonus subspecies *brittaniae* (Verity, 1915)

Although also known as the Hedge Brown, it is easy to understand why those who have an acquaintance with this agile, attractive, medium-sized satyrid prefer to call it the Gatekeeper. Its preferred habitat is a bramble-strewn hedgerow where it appears to exhibit strong territorial instincts. Flitting along the hedge for ten or twenty metres or so, it then retraces its path seemingly all the time the sun is shining and, if there is a gate in the hedge, the quiet observer will notice it passing and re-passing the spot—hence Gatekeeper.

It is attracted to the flowers of the bramble and also to those of wood sage, *Teucrium scorodonia,* and of marjoram, *Origanum vulgare.* The distribution of this butterfly in Ireland is, with extremely few exceptions, to the south of a line from Kerry to Dublin. There are two or three localities on the east coast (near Dublin) and in Co. Wicklow. The distribution in the south is generally coastal mainly centred around Co. Cork and Co. Waterford.

ADULT (Fig. 41D, Plate III B,C)
The expanded wings measure 40 mm in the male and 47 mm in the female. The ground colour is fulvous—a colour-term often used by the lepidopterist denoting a rich orange-brown. All the wings have a broad margin of

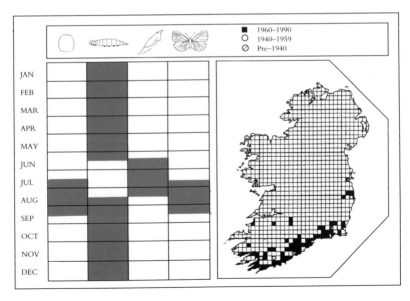

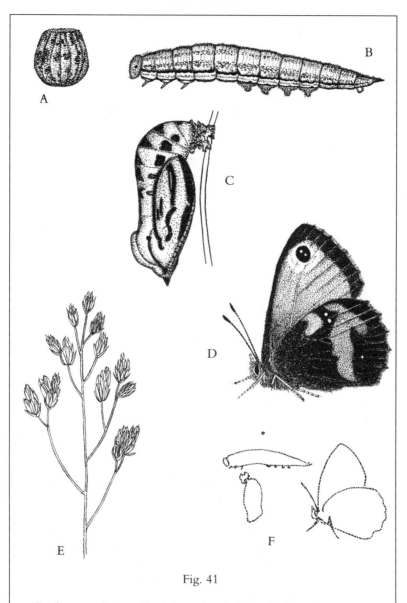

Fig. 41

Gatekeeper: A - Egg (ht. 0.65mm); B - Larva (L 23mm);
C - Pupa (L 12mm): D - Adult, side-view (wing-span m. 40mm,
f. 47mm); E - Food plant: cock's foot grass, *Dactylis glomerata;*
F - Life size.

fuscous-brown, except the front margin of the forewings, which is narrower. Fuscous is another colour-term used by the lepidopterist meaning 'dusky'.

In the case of the male only, there is a broad oblique bar near the centre of the forewings and a patch of androconial scales within the bar. In both sexes there is a black eye-mark with two white pupils near the apex, but in the fulvous area. The hindwings have a central fulvous area and a small eye-mark near the anal angle.

The female, however, is generally brighter in colour than the male. The hindwings have the basal half and the outer edge fulvous, and between the two is an irregular, light ochreous area in which four or five white-pupilled eye-spots are situated. This is a very variable species.

EGG (Fig. 41A)

The egg is proportionately small compared with the size of the adult butterfly, being only 0.65 mm both in height and in width. It is flattened at the top and bottom, being widest near the base and narrowing towards the summit. There are generally 16 longitudinal ridges, the intervals between the latter being concave, with about 14 transverse ribs in each. Where the ridges meet at the micropyle, they form a reticulated pattern. When first laid the egg is yellow, but it soon turns pearly-white and irregular rusty-red markings become evident after about 4 days. These markings then turn greyish-brown. The egg stage lasts about 20 days or so.

LARVA (Fig. 41B)

When fully-grown, which is usually at about 240 days in this stage, this slug-shaped larva is about 23 mm in length. The slug-like appearance is enhanced by the inconspicuous intersegmental divisions as well as the subdivisions. The head is bilobed. The ground colour is pale greenish-brown, and the mid-dorsal longitudinal stripe is olive-black. On each side is a wavy band of 'claret' marks adjacent to a pale stripe, and below this, again, is a darker claret stripe and a narrow line of the same colour. Microscopically, the surface of the body is covered with white serrated and bifurcate bristles. There is great variation in the intensity of colouration, both of ground colour and markings. In habit, like many satyrids, the larva is nocturnal, feeding at the tip of the grass stems and retiring to rest amongst the old leaf-bases during the day. There it takes up a position by lying lengthways along the brownish leaf-base, which closely resembles its own colouration.

The larva feeds on various grass species including annual meadow grass, *Poa annua*, couch grass, *Agropyron repens*, and cock's foot, *Dactylis glomerata*.

PUPA (Fig. 41C)

Pupation takes place around the end of June when a silk pad is spun on a grass stem. The pupa is attached to it by prong-tipped hairs arising from the cast skin which remains attached to the ventral surface of the abdomen. The cremastral area of the pupa is without hooks.

The pupa is from 11 mm to 12.7 mm in length and appears proportionately stout. Viewed from the top the head is truncated with pronounced angles on each side. The thorax is roughly parallel with the base of the wings and angular. From the side the wing-cases are prominent and convex.

The ground colour is creamy grey-brown with sometimes a greenish tinge. There is a strong pattern of conspicuous brownish-black marks, chief of which appear as longitudinal streaks on the wings. A series of blotches occurs on the thorax and abdomen. Microscopically, the general surface is covered with knobbed bristles.

The pupal stage lasts for approximately 22 days.

MEADOW BROWN

Maniola jurtina subspecies *iernes* Graves, 1930

This fairly large and rather sombre butterfly is one of the most widely distributed and abundant of Irish butterflies. Away from the mainland it is recorded from the Atlantic islands of Galway and Donegal. The Irish butterfly is a distinct subspecies named *iernes*, in which the yellowish-fulvous patches on the forewings of both sexes are larger than in the case of the British examples. Specimens resembling the latter, however, frequently occur.

The flight is rather feeble and fluttering, and the butterfly seldom flies high. It is easily disturbed, even in dull weather.

ADULT (Fig 42D, Plate III H,J)
The distance between the tips of the outstretched wings is 50 mm in the male and 55 mm in the female. The sexes are so very different that Linnaeus described them as two distinct species.

The ground colour of the male is a smokey fuscous-brown with bronze and greenish iridescence. There is an oblique black patch containing androconial scales, whilst near the apex there is a white-pupilled eye-spot with an outer ring of fulvous, which is more or less distinct. Beneath the eye-spot there is a fulvous area, rather clouded and variable in extent.

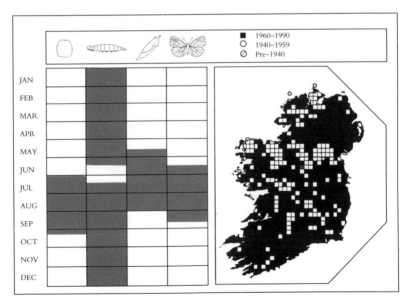

148

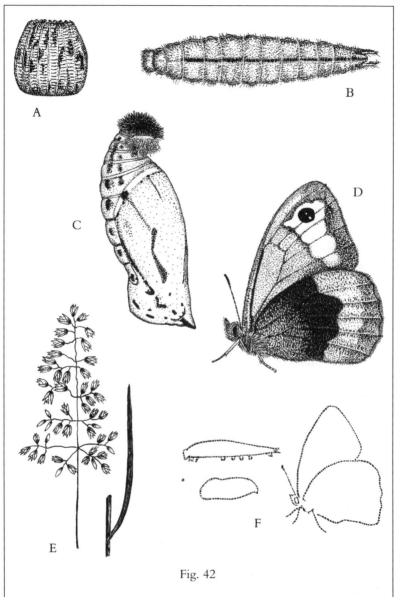

Fig. 42

Meadow Brown: A - Egg (ht. 0.5mm); B - Larva, view form above (L 25.5mm); C - Pupa (L 6.3mm) D - Adult side-view (wing-span m. 50mm, f. 55mm); E - Food plant: Meadow grass, *Poa pratensis*; F - Life size.

In the female the eye-spot is generally larger and is situated within a large, orange, fulvous, triangular area, broadest near the front margin. The area between this and the base of the wing is suffused, to a greater or lesser extent, with fulvous of a rather darker hue. The oblique black patch is absent in the female. The underside of the hindwings is dark brown near the base, greyish-brown near the outer margin, with a lighter band between the two.

This is a variable species with a strong tendency for 'bleaching'—a loss of pigment from areas of the wings.

EGG (Fig. 42A)

The egg is laid singly on a blade of grass. It is very small compared with the size of the adult butterfly, being only about 0.5 mm in height and the same in width. It appears as an approximate truncated cone, rounded at the base, but the top of the egg is flat. There are a number (20-24) of fairly prominent longitudinal ridges, which originate from the concentric ridges encircling the micropyle, and the troughs between the ridges are conspicuously concave. The troughs, or furrows, are transversely marked with about 24 ribs. At first the egg is pale yellow in colour, but it then becomes a rather stronger yellow, followed by a mottling with rust-red which gradually becomes darker, as does the ground colour. The length of the egg stage varies widely according to temperature and is from 2 to 4 weeks or so.

LARVA (Fig. 42B)

When fully grown (usually about the middle of April) the larva is about 25.5 mm in length. In shape, the body is stoutest in the middle segments, attenuating to a greater degree in the hinder segments. The ground colour of the upper surface is bright, almost translucent, green, whilst that of the lower surface is a rather darker green. Dividing the two surfaces is a 'lateral' line which is white, and under the lens is found to follow the curvature of the segments and their subdivision in a series of crescents, and terminates in the anal points. The legs are pale in colour and the very small spiracles are orange. There is a median dorsal, dark green stripe starting from the first abdominal segment and extending to the anal segment.

The whole body surface is covered with fine, grey and black, backwardly-curving hairs. The larvae grow only very slowly over the winter months, and this stage extends over about 250 days. They feed only at night on various grasses (of which *Poa annua* and *Poa pratensis* are the most important) and spend the days on the lower stems. In captivity, an individual larva will sometimes feed up to full growth by October and then pupate, as did one reared by the author.

PUPA (Fig. 42C)

A pad of silk is spun, onto which the larva suspends itself by the anal claspers. The average length of the pupa is almost 16 mm, and it is very stout in appearance, being about 6.3 mm in width at about the middle. The apex of the head consists of two blunt pyramids which slope inwards to form a 'waist'. The abdomen then swells out before diminishing abruptly to a stalk, at the apex of which is a dense tuft of spine-bearing hairs. These hairs become entangled with the silk of the pad, firmly securing the pupa. Seen from above, the 'shoulders' of the thorax bear blunt projections.

The ground colour of the pupa is a clear translucent green which is speckled and blotched with pale yellow. The centre line of the upper surface, as well as the head, limbs and wing-cases, are reticulated also with pale yellow. The whole pupa is spotted and barred with black and brown.

The pupal stage lasts from 25 to 30 days.

RINGLET

Aphantopus hyperantus (Linnaeus, 1758)

Like the Speckled Wood butterfly, the Ringlet prefers the shady edges of woodland, but also damp meadows, rough hillsides and marshy areas. It is not so agile as the Speckled Wood and is single-brooded; whereas the latter species produces several broods annually.

In spite of the somewhat sooty colour of the upper-wing surface, when freshly emerged and flying, the 'eyes' on the underside do not show; but the marginal line of white scales can easily be seen, making identification quite simple in flight.

Although occurring widely throughout Ireland, the distribution map shows fairly large gaps.

ADULT (Fig. 43D, Plate III L)
The wings when outstretched measure 48 mm in the male and 52 mm in the female.

In the male, the ground colour of the wings is very dark velvety-brown, almost black. There is an area of very nearly black androconial scales situated at the base of the forewings which are difficult to define on account of the general colouration. Towards the centre of both fore- and hindwings there are two to

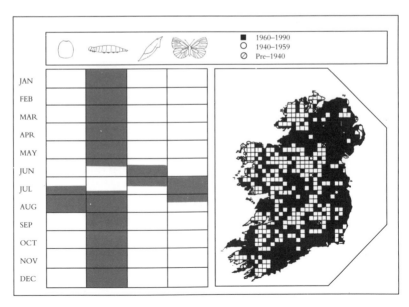

152

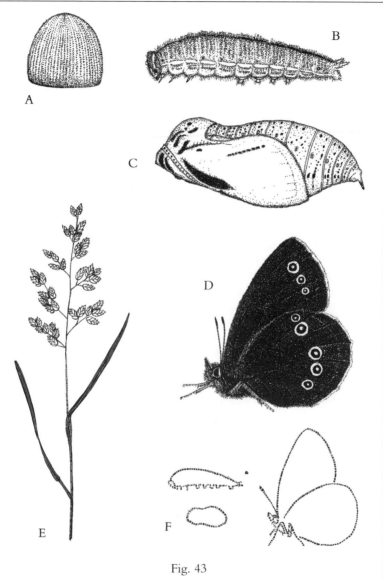

Fig. 43

Ringlet: A - Egg (ht. 0.8mm); B - Larva (L 20.5mm); C - Pupa (L 11-12.7mm); D - Adult side-view (wing-span m.48mm, f. 52mm); E - Food plant: Annual meadow grass, *Poa annua*; F - Life size.

three black eye-spots. These have faint, light pupils and are ringed with rather dusky yellow. The underside is lighter in colour, being chocolate-brown with two or three black eye-spots on the forewing, and five on the hindwing. These have white pupils and are ringed with yellow. The pair near the front margin of the hindwing is united. All wings possess an indistinct brown line very near to, and parallel with, the outer margin.

In the larger female, the ground colour is generally lighter and the eye-spotting more distinct.

This is a very variable species in respect of the eye-spotting.

EGG (Fig. 43A)

This measures 0.80 mm wide at the base and is a little less than this in height. It is dome-shaped but the base is concave. The surface has a varnished appearance and bears a fine honeycomb-like pattern which runs in streaks from the base to the crown. When freshly laid it is light yellow, but gradually darkens, and after seven days the colour is pale lilac-buff. Immediately before hatching it darkens again and the embryo larva is visible through the clear shell.

The eggs do not adhere to the blades of grass on which they are laid, but fall down and lie loosely amongst the roots.

LARVA (Fig. 43B)

When fully grown the larva is about 20-21 mm in length and has a hunched-up appearance. The body extends, however, when the larva is walking, which it does only slowly. The brown head is covered with small tubercles (granulated) on each of which is a fine hair. There is a light-coloured streak on each side of the head, at the base of which is situated the dark-coloured eye. The ground colour is very light brown, tinged with pink. There is a dark brown median dorsal line, indistinct and broken up in the anterior segments, but distinct and darker in the hind segments. The last spiracle is enlarged. A pale whitish band extends along each side together with a dark brown line below it—more distinct at the hinder end. The whole body is covered with variously sized hairs, of which the larger ones are brown and the smaller ones whitish. It feeds only at night on a number of grass species, including annual meadow grass, *Poa annua*, and cock's-foot, *Dactylis glomerata*. This species appears to require a damp environment in nature, although when reared, a 'dry' state is the only one possible, as the winter is passed as small larvae and in damper conditions is invaded by mould.

PUPA (Fig. 43C)

There is a little difference in size between male and female pupae. Whereas the male is about 11 mm in length, the female is about 12.7 mm, but both have a dumpy appearance without much in the way of angular projections, except for the terminal segment which is sharp, hook-shaped, and bending downwards, terminating in a few minute spines. The pupa is widest near the tips of the wings and the antennae form a keel. The ground colour is pale creamy-brown, whilst the abdominal segments are spotted and banded with dark brown spots of two distinct sizes. Two black bands run over the eye and continue down the legs on the inside edge of the antennae. The spiracles are light brown. The pupal stage lasts about 14 days.

SMALL HEATH

Coenonympha pamphilus (Linnaeus, 1758)

This is generally an abundant butterfly and, although fairly widespread, appears to be more plentiful in widely scattered areas near the coast.

It occurs in a number of types of grassy situations. Sometimes it is observed in numbers in dull weather or the late evening, when they tend to congregate at the tops of grassy stems. It always rests with its wings held vertically. Although not generally believed to be a migrant species, the Small Heath has, on occasions, been observed coming in from the sea. It is quite active on dull, warm days, and has been recorded as occurring in mountainous districts up to a height of 800 m.

ADULT (Fig. 44D, Plate III M)
The outstretched wings of the male measure 33 mm, whilst those of the female measure 37 mm. The ground colour of the wings is described as pale-tawny and there is a greyish-brown or smokey border around all the wings. This is accentuated in the male and may be almost absent in the female. There is a black spot near the apex of the forewing and a minute, light-coloured pupil may be present. The inner-half of the hindwing is grey and bordered by a curved pale band. On the underside, the forewings are

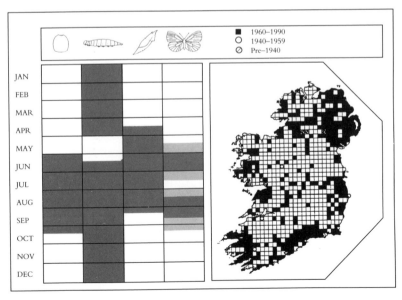

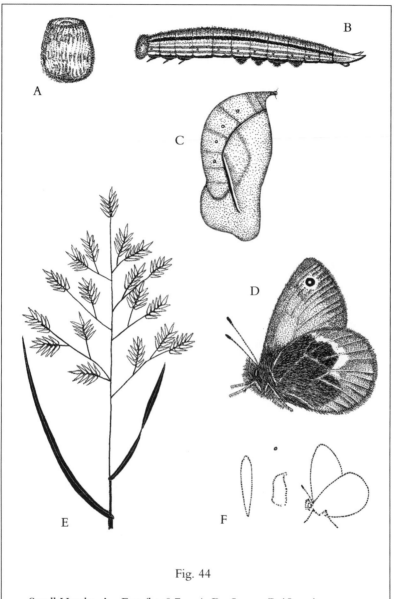

Fig. 44

Small Heath: A - Egg (ht. 0.7mm) B - Larva, (L 19mm);
C - Pupa (L 8.5mm); D - Adult side-view (wing-span m. 33mm,
f. 37mm); E - Food plant: Meadow fescue, *Festuca pratensis*;
F - Life size.

rather darker than the upper. The eye-spot is pupilled, ringed with yellow, and separated from the inner-half of the wings by a brownish-grey streak. The hindwing is generally greyish, with the basal-half brownish and clothed with long fine hairs. A curved, light-coloured band separates the outer greyish margin with four indistinct eye-spots ringed with rusty-brown. This is a very variable species.

EGG (Fig. 44A)

The size of the egg of this species is relatively large for such a small butterfly, being about 0.7 mm in height and just a little less at the greatest width. There are a number of more or less vertical ridges with minute horizontal reticulations. The top of the egg is depressed, but there is a central protuberant 'boss', which does not reach the height of the outer rim. This area is minutely pitted 'like a thimble'.

The sides of the egg are convex and the base rounded. When first laid the egg is light green in colour, but it gradually changes to a buffish tone with purplish-grey zones and bands. Just before hatching the shell becomes translucent with the embryo larva visible within.

The length of the egg stage varies from twelve to sixteen days.

LARVA (Fig. 44B)

The young larvae feed until after the third moult, which occurs generally about the end of September, and then hibernate. During warm weather, however, they will recommence feeding. Like many satyrids, the larva walks very slowly and feeds on the top of the grass leaf during darkness, returning to rest at the base of the plant during daytime. After hibernation, however, feeding takes place in daylight. On being disturbed, both ends of the body are curled upwards whilst the middle claspers hold onto the grass stem. If disturbed further, the larva will fall to the ground but curled up the opposite way!

The fully grown larva is about 19 mm in length when crawling, but is about 3 mm less when resting. The body is attenuated both in front and behind, being widest at the fourth segment. The head is larger than the first segment. The anal points are pink and covered with short white spines. Whilst the ground colour of the upper surface is yellowish-green, the underneath is dark green. There are three dark green longitudinal stripes, all bordered with whitish, and the mid-dorsal stripe is wider and rather darker. The spiracular stripe is light brownish-green and a very pale-coloured line joins the spiracles. Another yellowish-green stripe traverses the whole length of the body beneath the spiracular line. The whole body surface, including the green head, is covered with minute, curved spines each arising from a white protuberance.

The larva feeds on various grass species, principally on annual meadow grass, *Poa annua*, crested dog's tail, *Cynosurus cristatus*, and mat grass, *Nardus stricta*.

When fully fed the larva spins a pad of silk on a grass stem, and after hanging from it by the anal claspers, metamorphoses into a pupa.

As there are possibly two, three or more overlapping life cycles of the Small Heath in the year, the length of the larval stage may vary widely from as long as 10 months to as little as 4 months. However, confirmation is required as to the significance of the different 'broods' of this species.

PUPA (Fig. 44C)

This is about 8.5 mm in length and 5 mm in width, measured from the side. The head has a truncated appearance and the thorax is rather bulbous, as is the abdomen, which is curved downwards. The anal segment terminates in a prominent, flattened cremaster which is rectangular when viewed from above. A large number of cremastral hooks, arise from the tip. These consist of a long shank and a small recurved hook, bright amber in colour.

The ground colour of the pupa is brilliant green, but under the lens appears whitish-green sprinkled with dark green spots. The abdomen shows a longitudinal mid-dorsal stripe of dark green spots which is continued over the thorax as a narrow darker line. The cremaster is yellowish-brown with a pinkish tinge and a dark brown lateral band.

The length of the pupal stage is about 26 days.

LARGE HEATH

Coenonympha tullia (Müller, 1764)

The great variation which occurs in this satyrid has given rise to much confusion in the past—particularly with naming. Formerly, specific rank was given to several races which are today recognised as subspecies of a single species; however, this species is extremely variable even within individual populations, and use of sub-specific names can be wrought with frustration. Such names would perhaps be best applied as names of forms, i.e. f. *scotica*; Staudinger; f. *polyclama* (Haworth).

In Ireland two 'subspecies' are recognised and these are *scotica* and *polydama,* which are described later. There is also confusion as to the larval food plant. The adult butterfly is fairly closely restricted to raised and blanket bogs, damp moors and hillsides—sometimes at considerable elevation. On the other hand, it is found at not much above sea-level, where these conditions prevail. In the wild, oviposition has been observed taking place on the beaked rush, *Rhynchospora alba*, and it has been thought that this plant is its preferred food. Common cotton-grass, *Eriophorum,* occurs widely in areas where the butterfly occurs and this is also given as a food plant. In captivity the larva will feed on a wide variety of grass species, so it might be assumed that it will do so in the wild.

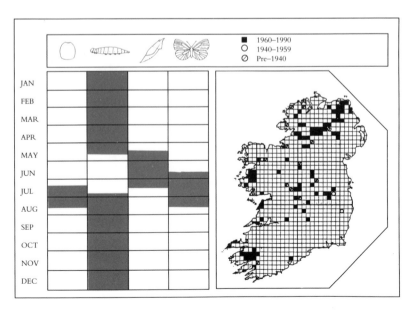

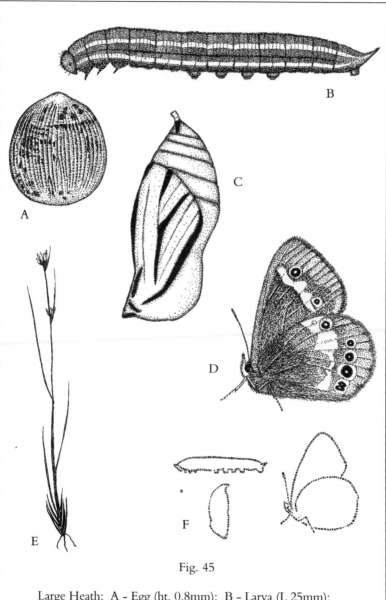

Fig. 45

Large Heath: A - Egg (ht. 0.8mm); B - Larva (L 25mm);
C - Pupa (L 11mm); D - Adult, side-view (wing-span
41mm); E - food plant: Beaked rush, *Rhynochspora alba*;
F - Life size.

The adult is sometimes seen to be blown considerable distances by the wind, belying its deceptively weak flight, but it is capable of beating back against the wind.

Flowers have little attraction for it. It is distributed fairly widely and is locally abundant, but absent from most eastern and southern coastal areas. It is probably doomed to disappear from its midland haunts as bog exploitation continues.

ADULT (Fig. 45D, Plate III K)

This butterfly is small to medium in size, being smaller than most satyrids, but larger than the Small Heath, which it resembles. The average distance across the wings is about 41 mm. The sexes are similar except that the female is slightly or much lighter in colour. In f. *polydama*, the upperside of the forewings is fulvous-brown; rather more golden towards the base, and there is a transverse yellowish bar stretching more than half-way across the wing. Between the bar and the apex is an eye-spot of yellowish-brown with a black centre. There is sometimes a less conspicuous one near the inner angle. Indeed, additional yellowish-brown spots may be present.

The hindwing is generally darker in colour and a varying number of eyespots—from 1 to 3 or more—are also present. On the underside, the outer margins of the fore- and hindwings are grey, with the transverse band more pronounced on the forewing. In the hindwing there is an irregular white band across the middle and the basal area is bluish-green with a series of about 6 more or less conspicuous eye-spots towards the outer margin.

In f. *scotica* the eye-spots both on the upper and under surfaces are very inconspicuous, indeed, sometimes almost non-existent. Although Ford (1945) says that *scotica* occurs in Ireland, Hillis (*pers. comm.*) states that he has never seen it. In fact it is widespread in Ireland mainly in the south and west. F. *polydama* occurs in many parts of the country: however, its main stronghold appears to be in the midlands and north.

The adult is on the wing from the middle of June to end of July according to season, but the actual flight season is very short, so that it is probably under-recorded.

EGG (Fig. 45A)

Comparatively large for the size of the adult, the egg measures about 0.8 mm in height. It is an elliptic spheroid, but the finely reticulated micropyle at the apex is swollen. The surface is also finely reticulated at the apex, where about fifty longitudinal irregular ridges originate and, after running over the side of the egg, disappear near the base. There is a pattern of very fine, transverse ribbing between the ridges. When freshly laid the egg is a very light brownish-green. It then becomes yellowish and later brown spots and blotches appear, some of which form a band around the egg a little distance from the apex. Shortly before hatching the egg becomes opalescent.

The egg stage lasts about fourteen days.

LARVA (Fig. 45B)

The fully grown larva is a little over 25 mm in length and, like all satyrids, is widest at about one-third of its length from the head. It diminishes in width towards the head, but is more intensely attenuated towards the hinder end. The dual 'points' are rose-pink. The intersegmental divisions are ill-defined.

The ground colour is grass green, whilst the mid-dorsal longitudinal stripe is very dark green bordered with white. The sub-dorsal stripes are palest yellow and terminate at the anal points. There is a white sub-spiracular stripe and between these latter two stripes is a dark green, irregular, thin subcutaneous line. The head is green as is the underside of the larva.

After second moult (in the third instar), usually during September, the larva hibernates and resumes feeding in March. Progression up and down the food plant stems is extremely sluggish and on the slightest disturbance the larva falls to the ground.

PUPA (Fig. 45C)

This is about 11 mm in length and attached by a hooked cremaster to a silk pad woven onto the plant stem. Frohawk describes this as 'elegantly proportioned'. The thorax is humped, giving a waist between it and the slightly curved abdomen. At first it is a 'vivid translucent green' but gradually becomes a brilliant emerald green. Finally it becomes duller and deeper in colour.

This stage lasts about 23 days.

COMMON MIGRANT SPECIES

CLOUDED YELLOW

Colias croceus (Geoffroy, in Fourcroy, 1785)

The sub-family COLIADINAE includes two migrant species, the present one and the Pale Clouded Yellow, *Colias hyale,* which have been recorded in Ireland. Both are migrants, but whereas *C.croceus* occurs most years (sometimes in abundance), *C.hyale* is very rare. Years of abundance of *C.croceus* are known as 'Edusa' years, this being the old specific name superceded under the laws of priority by *croceus.*

The Irish population is entirely dependent on a wave of fresh immigrants from North Africa and southern Europe. Those arriving in early summer are very productive and large numbers often emerge in August and September. These lay, but no matter what stage is reached by the broods, they are wiped out at the beginning of winter.

Distribution is somewhat as might be expected, with most sightings on the southeast coast, fewer on the east coast and but sparingly elsewhere. One of the easiest butterflies to identify on the wing, it is, nevertheless, a very fast flier.

ADULT (Fig. 46D, Plate III O,P)
The ground colour is orange or orange-yellow with a broad, black border to all wings, which are dusted with yellow scales on emergence, but which are soon lost. Near the centre of the forewings there is a black, discoidal spot and on the hindwings, near the middle, is an orange mark not unlike the figure '8'. The female may be identified by the black borders being spotted with yellow to a greater or lesser degree. Often some of the veins, as they pass through the black bands, are marked with yellow. In both sexes the hindwings are darker than the forewings and show a greenish tinge. The antennae are rather robust and have a pinkish tinge as also have the closely adjacent areas. The distance across the expanded wings is about 55 mm.

This species is most variable in its ground colour. The females extremely so, being every shade of orange through to light yellow to white. A form of the female which is not uncommon has the orange colour of the wings replaced by light yellow. It is known as *f.helice* Hübner. Many males show the hindwings shot with amethyst-blue. This is known as *ab.purpurescens* Cockerell.

EGG (Fig. 46A)
The egg is vase- or spindle-shaped, the basal half being slightly stouter than the apex. It measures about 1.1 mm in height and is about 0.5 mm in diameter at

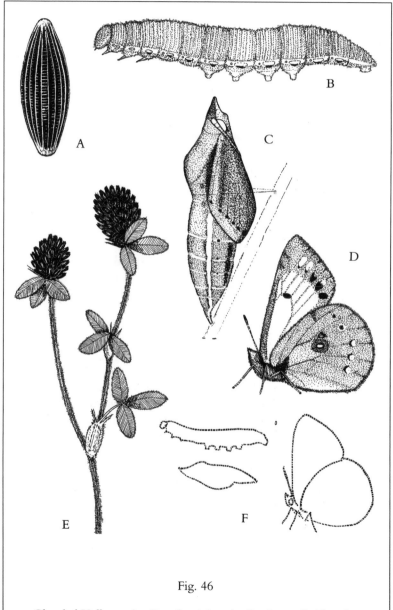

Fig. 46

Clouded Yellow: A - Egg (ht. 1.1mm); B - Larva (L 32mm);
C - Pupa (L 20mm); D - Adult, side-view (wing- 1span 51mm)
E - Food plant: Red clover, *Trifolium pratense*; F - Life size.

the middle. The micropyle is situated at the apex, which is somewhat depressed. At first the egg is yellow in colour, then 'copper-pink', and then 'rosy-orange-pink', but the apex and the base are yellow throughout. About 20 longitudinal ridges follow the shape of the egg, most of them running the entire length. There are about 38 minute transverse ribs. The length of the egg stage varies from about six days to ten according to temperature.

LARVA (Fig. 46B)

Up to about 32 mm in length, it is generally cylindrical but tapering at the thoracic segments and the three terminal segments. The head is relatively small. The ground colour is a deep apple-green and the surface texture is of fine velvet. This is caused by a series of transverse rings—about five per segment— covering the whole body. Each ring bears minute light-coloured spots, each of which has a short black hair. The spiracular line is conspicuous and usually of a clear yellow, but it may be whitish, and each segment bears a red blotch on the spiracular line, with a smaller black mark below it.

The larva is slow-moving, almost slug-like, and it feeds on species of clover, *Trifolium* spp., trefoil, *Lotus* and other related species. The larvae are to be found in June and the second brood in September and October, but the late larvae, however, do not survive.

The length of the larval stage varies from 5–7 weeks according to pre-vailing temperatures.

PUPA (Fig. 46C)

Usually about 20 mm in length, its ground colour is a light, almost translus-cent, green. There is a mid-dorsal dark-green line which is more conspicuous at the front, and the thorax is darker at the front also. There is a mid-lateral line which is yellow (similar to that of the larva) and edged dorsally with dark-green. This line is continued above the wing-cases. The head is also dark-green, the top of the 'rostrum' being *very* dark, but the lower part is yellow.

The wing-cases are generally dark-green, but there are five small, black spots arranged transversely near the outer margin of the wing and others in the centre of the wing. The lower abdomen is yellowish but bears four black spots on the abdominal segments which are variable in size. In addition, there are larger black blotches lying beneath them which join to form a continuous band.

There is a yellowish cremaster fixed to a silken pad and also there is a fine silk girdle.

The pupal stage lasts about 17 days.

RED ADMIRAL

Vanessa atalanta (Linnaeus, 1758)

This large, attractive butterfly, attired on its upper surface in rich black velvet and brilliant orange-red, is Irish only as an immigrant. There is little evidence that any hibernate over the winter months, but large numbers fly over from Europe in late spring and early summer. Their progeny are seen in late summer and autumn and, indeed, are often observed as late as November sucking nectar from late-flowering plants or the juices of fermenting fruit. They appear to make no reconnaisance for hibernating sites as does the Small Tortoiseshell. There have been suggestions that there is a southwards migration in the autumn, such as was noted in 1989 (Haynes & Lavery, 1990).

Unlike a number of its near-related species which lay their eggs in clusters, the Red Admiral lays a single egg at a time so that it may wander over considerable distances.

ADULT (Fig. 47D, Plate III N)

The male measures about 67 mm and the female about 72 mm across the out-stretched wings. The sexes are very similar. The ground colour is rich, velvety black, and on the forewings there is a broad, orange-scarlet band from near the anal angle, transversely to the front margin about one-third of its length from the base of the wing. Between the orange-scarlet band and the apex is a snow-white, bar-like mark which meets the front margin, and five smaller white marks. The outer margin is scalloped, and there are three small spots of a lilac colour near the apex and two lunules of similar colour beneath them. The hind-wing bears a broad, scarlet band around the outer margin and has four black spots centrally, whilst there is a black-edged bar at the anal angle.

On the underside the forewing is similarly patterned to the upper surface, but there is much blue and the scarlet band is yellow towards the outer angle. The hindwing is intricately reticulated in many colours, including maroon and blue, and there is a band of light, creamy-brown near the hind margin and a number of patches of the same colour on the front margin.

EGG (Fig. 47A)

The egg is very small for such a large and robust butterfly, being only 0.8 mm in height. It is upright oval in shape and somewhat cylindrical for about the lower three-quarters and conical at the upper quarter. A conspicuous feature shared by many of the NYMPHALIDAE is the presence of 9 or so longitudinal flange-like ridges or 'keels'. These are white and glossy with transverse

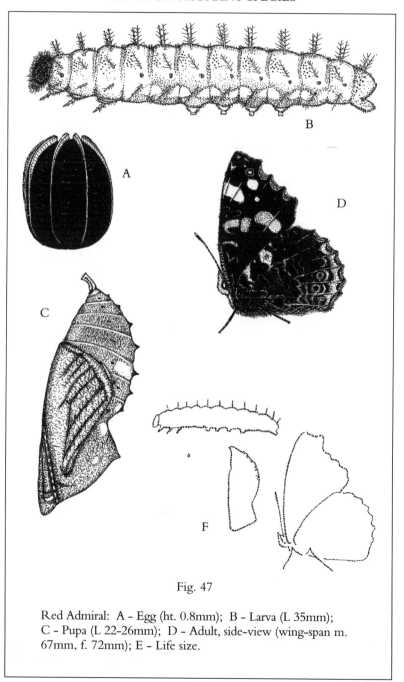

Fig. 47

Red Admiral: A - Egg (ht. 0.8mm); B - Larva (L 35mm);
C - Pupa (L 22-26mm); D - Adult, side-view (wing-span m.
67mm, f. 72mm); E - Life size.

flutings, being deepest at the apex, where they extend over towards the micropyle. Between the keels, the spaces are concave with barely discernible transverse markings. It is light-green in colour at first, becoming more yellowish until just before hatching, when it turns a pearly-grey with the dark head of the larva apparent.

The eggs are laid singly on the tops of the terminal leaves of stinging nettle, *Urtica dioica*, and the egg stage lasts about one week, but may vary from 5 to 10 days. In captivity, however, the eggs have been laid on cardboard, nylon gauze and other materials, as well as several being laid on a single nettle leaf.

LARVA (Fig. 47B)

The young larva emerges from the egg by biting an exit hole in the crown and is only about 1.6 mm in length. It is light yellowish-green in colour and in the course of 23 days or so grows to a length of about 35 mm, undergoing 4 moults in the process. It is stout in appearance but tapers somewhat towards the front. It lives a solitary life within the shelter of a single leaf whose edges have been drawn together with silk. When resting it coils itself into a figure 6, but when feeding it eats the shelter-leaf and, when this is partially consumed it moves to another nearby, constructing another shelter. In colour it is extremely variable. One specimen collected by the author was pale greenish-grey whilst others were velvety-black, but in each case there was a series of moon-shaped yellow patches along the sides, with each patch divided by the division between the segments. As in all the NYMPHALIDAE, the body is covered with branched spines. In the present species there is a series of 7 rows running along the body and a single row running down the centre of the back from the 4th to the 11th segments inclusive, and those on the sides of the body begin on the second segment. The whole body surface is covered with minute white warts, each of which bears a fine white hair. The head is black with a bronze sheen. The thoracic legs are black and shining, whilst the abdominal legs are light-brown.

PUPA (Fig. 47C)

When ready for pupation the fully fed larva draws 2 or 3 leaves of its food plant together with silken threads to form a shelter—sometimes securing further with a few 'guy-lines'. It then spins a pad of silk in the apex of the shelter to which the claspers are fixed. The larva then hangs vertically downwards but with the fore end of the body curled upwards, and the change to pupa takes place after about 3 days. Suspended now by its cremaster firmly attached to the silk pad by the numerous minute hooks, it measures from 22-26 mm in length. At first it is brownish with dark-green wing cases, but it then assumes a greyish colour, in some lights appearing purplish and bloom-like. Additionally, it is richly ornamented with spots of burnished gold in a line along the top of the hinder end of the abdomen and at the sides opposite the wing cases, including some of the pointed projections. Sometimes the wing cases are suffused with gold. If examined with a x10 lens, the whole surface of the pupa is seen to be covered with a fine reticulation of vein-like marks. The pupal stage lasts about 17 days and the pupae may be found from early in July to very late in the year.

PAINTED LADY

Cynthia cardui (Linnaeus, 1758)

In some years this immigrant butterfly is abundant. It is extremely widespread in southern Europe and North Africa where enormous populations are built up. They then periodically disperse northwards, producing migrations during successive generations. During May and June, in most years, a number reach Ireland and these produce an Irish generation later in the year. Under adverse climatic conditions later in the year, there is thought to be a tendency for a southwards migration. None survive the winter in Ireland in any stage.

In Ireland its records conform with expectations in that it has been observed mainly on the south and southeastern coasts.

ADULT (Fig. 48D, Plate III Q)
This butterfly measures across outstretched wings about 64 mm in the male and 70 mm in the female. Apart from size, the only observable difference is in the shape of the wings.

In the male, the apex of the forewing is more pointed and the outer margin of the hindwing less rounded than in the female. The ground colour is usually tawny-orange, but there is some variation in the amount of pinkish tinge or suffusion which may be present, especially when the butterfly is freshly emerged. The apex of the wing is black spotted with white, and three large angular patches of black form a more or less transverse band from the hind to the front margin. The basal area of the hindwings is black, whilst six arrow-shaped black spots are situated along the margin. Between the margin and the dark basal area, there is a parallel row of bars and another row of larger spots. A black-margined blue lunule occupies the anal angle.

On the underside, the apical area of the forewing is light brown and olive marked with white in a similar pattern to the upper surface, whilst the basal area is rosy, marked with black. The hindwing is beautifully mottled with brown, olive-brown and white. The veins are white and there are two large and two small eye-spots, violet and green margined with straw-yellow and black. Between the eye-spots and the margin there is a series of seven or eight lilac bars margined with black. The pale underside can assist identification at a distance.

EGG (Fig. 48A)
This is small for the size of the adult, being only about 0.65 mm in height. It is spherical in shape and stands on the long axis with its width greatest a little

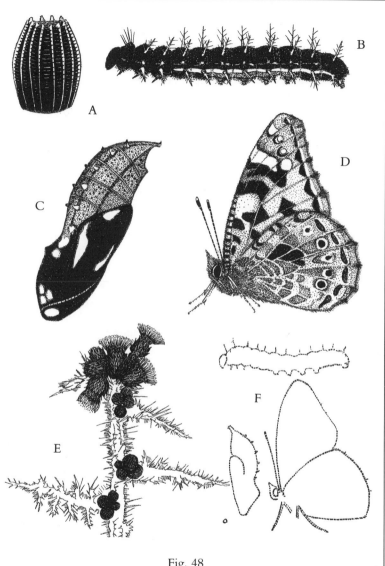

Fig. 48

Painted Lady: A - Egg (ht. 0.65mm); B - Larva (L 28.6mm);
C - Pupa (L 24mm); D - Adult, side-view (wing-span m.
64mm, f. 70mm); E - Food plant: Marsh thistle, *Cirsium palustre*.
F - Life size.

below the centre. There are sixteen fluted longitudinal ridges which are conspicuous and glassy-white. Towards the apex the ridges increase in depth before running over the apex into the micropyle, which lies in a depression. The transverse ribbing is very fine and not prominent.

Although recorded from a wide variety of plant species, the egg is usually laid singly on the leaf of a thistle species, *Carduus* spp. and *Cirsium* spp. When first laid, the egg ground colour is light-green and gradually becomes bottle-green until shortly before emergence when it changes to grey-green. The head of the embryonic larva shows through as deep grey.

The length of the egg stage is about seven days.

LARVA (Fig. 48B)

On hatching, the larva walks over the leaf to the underside where it spins a silken web over itself, as a cover, feeding on the lower epidermis of the leaf whilst leaving the upper epidermis as a cover. Up to the third moult the larva lives within the web, consuming only the lower leaf skin, but after the third moult it feeds ravenously on the whole leaf tissue, with the exception of the stronger spines. When fully fed it measures about 28.6 mm in length and, except for the third and fourth segments (which are marginally larger), it is uniform in thickness.

The colour of the entire upper surface is a velvety black but greyish at the intersegmental divisions. Commencing at the fourth segment and ending at the eleventh is a longitudinal lateral yellow stripe which takes up the form of a series of crescents, the sub-spiracular spines occupying the gaps between them. Behind each yellow-margined spiracle is a short yellow streak and variable yellow marks form a broken line above the white-outlined spiracles.

The under surface of the larva is reddish-brown and the legs a little darker. The whole body is covered with fine white hairs, each arising from a white spot. The hairs are short on the upper surface by comparison with those of the lateral and ventral surfaces.

A series of branched spines is present as follows.

There are no spines on the first segment, four spines on each of the second and third segments, with the remaining segments each having seven spines, except for the last, which has four spines. The colour of the spines is extremely variable, being from wholly yellow to almost entirely black. The head is dark grey and covered with black and whitish hairs, and there is a central longitudinal black line bordered with white-cream speckles.

The length of the larval stage is about 25 days.

PUPA (Fig. 48C)

When ready to pupate, the larva spins a small but compact pad of silk. It then attaches itself to the pad by the anal claspers. This may be on an adjacent stem or within the loose threads of silk on a thistle leaf. When the larval skin erupts, the cremaster twists free, fastening onto the pad so that the larval skin falls away. The pupa is about 24mm in length. From above the head is square, being widest at the thorax thereafter. The bases of the wings are angled, as also, but to a lesser extent, are the inner margins. The fifth and sixth segments are enlarged and the anal extremity is attenuated into a long, stalked cremaster. Seen from the side, the position of the larval spines is taken from a series of sharp points. There is wide variation in colouration. Ground colour may be grey, brownish-grey or greenish-grey but, according to the angle of viewing, there is a coppery golden or silver sheen. A pattern of blotches and stripes also occurs. The wings are purplish-brown with long pearly marks.

The pupal stage lasts about 14 days.

RARE MIGRANT SPECIES AND VAGRANTS

PALE CLOUDED YELLOW

Colias hyale (Linnaeus, 1758)

The first inclusion of this species in the Irish List was due to Kane, who recorded it as 'occurring sparingly in the South and at Howth, migrating thither with much larger numbers of *C.edusa*' in 1868. Baynes (1964) stated that he knew of no other reliable records. Three occurred in 1973 and two in 1974 along the south/southeast coast (Hillis, *pers. comm.*). This species is associated with the Clouded Yellow and often occurs with it, although in much smaller numbers, when migrating swarms are encountered. It is extremely unlikely that it would be able to survive the winter in any stage of its life cycle.

A few notes on the species, Berger's Clouded Yellow, *Colias alfacariensis* Berger, would be appropriate here. This species was first described as being distinct from the Pale Clouded Yellow in 1948. It is a known migrant and has been found in collections of the Pale Clouded Yellow in Britain, but has so far not yet been discovered in Ireland. It closely resembles the Pale Clouded Yellow but differs from it in having more rounded wings and the dark edge around the hindwings being almost absent, whilst the dark border to the forewings is much reduced.

ADULT (Fig. 49D, Plate IV B)
The Pale Clouded Yellow closely resembles the Clouded Yellow in size and shape of the wings and wing pattern, and it is not unlike the female Clouded Yellow. The male, however, has a primrose background whilst the female is creamy-white. The latter could be confused with the female *f.helice* of *C.croceus*, but the black border of the hindwings is not nearly so prominent. It measures about 50 mm across the expanded wings, but exceptionally large species are known measuring practically 60 mm. It could occur in May or June immediately after migration or in the autumn from eggs laid in early summer or, again, after migration.

EGG (Fig. 49A)
This resembles that of the Clouded Yellow and is also laid on clover, lucerne and some other plants of the family LEGUMINOSAE. It is 1.1mm in height.

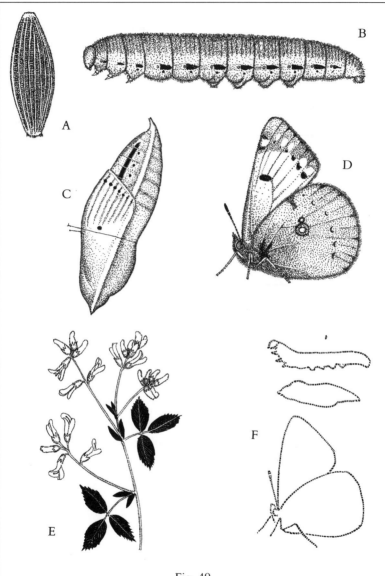

Fig. 49

Pale Clouded Yellow: A - Egg (ht. 1.1mm); B - Larva (l 32mm)
C - Pupa (L 21mm); D - Adult side-view (wing-span 50mm);
E - Food Plant: Lucerne, *Medicago sativa*; F - Life size.

LARVA (Fig. 49B)

The larva differs from that of the Clouded Yellow in having the spiracular stripe rather more brownish and the post-spiracular red bar conspicuously running to the intersegmental groove of each segment.

It is 32 mm in length when fully grown.

PUPA (Fig. 49C)

This can be distinguished by the ventral surface of the abdomen, being reddish and not green as in the Clouded Yellow.

It is 20-22 mm in length.

BATH WHITE

Pontia daplidice (Linnaeus, 1758)

The migrant Bath White has been recorded in Ireland on only six occasions—1893 being the first at Courtown, Co Wexford, with four next in 1945 (Kerry), and one in 1946 (Kerry). In 1945 in England, 650 were recorded, the majority from Cornwall, so that the four which were all taken in Waterville, Co Kerry, probably represent a small percentage of the specimens flying in Ireland that year. It has been noted that of wild-laid eggs, only about 0.1% reached maturity. This is on account of the extremely high rate of predation by red mites and small weevils feeding on the eggs, as well as parasitation by the exceedingly abundant hymenopteron, *Apanteles glomeratus.*

ADULT (Fig. 50D, Plate IV A)
When on the wing, this butterfly is more likely to be taken for the Small White, Green-veined White or the female of the Orange-tip. Indeed, the undersides of the hindwings are mottled with green like the latter species, but the mottling is much greener and less fragmented.

On the upper side of the forewings the apical black area is broken up by four white blotches. There is a large black spot situated at the outer extremity of the discoidal cell and extending beyond it. The outer vein of the cell bisects the spot and shows up as a white line.

In the female, the black marks on the forewing are more intense, and there is an additional lunate mark in the centre of the lower half of the wing between veins 1 and 2. The dark marking of the upper side of the hindwings around the outer edge is intensely black.

The wingspan measures 50 mm.

EGG (Fig. 50A)
Eggs are laid on the various species of mignonette, RESEDACEAE, often on the flower. Closely resembling the anther of garden mignonette, *Reseda odorata*, the egg is similar to that of the Orange-tip, but without the rather elongated apex, and with *all* the longitudinal ridges running the entire length of the egg, instead of some failing to reach the apex as in the Orange-Tip. It is 0.86 mm in height. Some species of CRUCIFERAE, eg. sea radish, *Raphanus maritimus*, and hedge mustard, *Sisymbrium officinale*, are given as plants on which eggs have been found.

The egg stage lasts about 10 days.

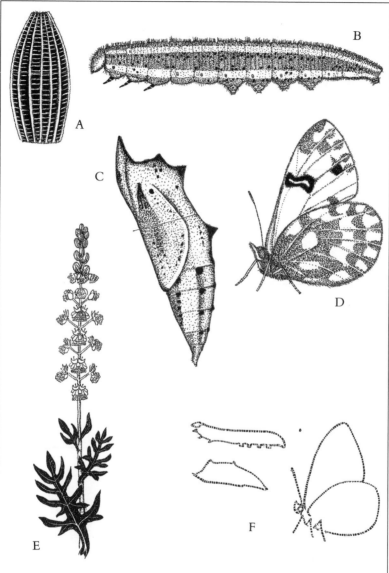

Fig. 50

Bath White: A - Egg (ht. 0.86mm); B - Larva (L 25.4mm);
C - Pupa (L 19mm); D - Adult side-view (wing-span 50mm);
E - Food plant Garden mignonette, *Reseda odorata*; F - Life size.

185

LARVA (Fig. 50B)

The ground colour is bluish-grey with yellow, or whitish spotted with yellow, longitudinal stripes. The black-spotted, yellow head is rather hairy.

The larval stage lasts for about 4 weeks. It measures 25.4 mm in length.

PUPA (Fig. 50C)

Variable in colour, the pupa can be bluish-grey, whitish, green, fawn or buff. Just before emergence, however, it becomes pale grey. It is 19 mm in length.

The pupal stage is from 10 to 14 days.

AMERICAN PAINTED LADY

Cynthia virginiensis (Drury, 1773)

Only three specimens of this species have been recorded as being found in Ireland—one near Cork in 1901, one in 1929 at Timoleague in Co. Cork, and one in the following year in Killarney, Co. Kerry.

It is a wide-ranging species and a well-known wanderer throughout North and Central America, as well as Hawaii and the Canary Isles. It is probable that the Irish specimens originated in the latter.

This species is also referred to as Hunter's butterfly and was at one time known as *C.huntera*, and has also been placed in the genera *Pyrameis* and *Vanessa*. It is one of the eight butterfly species found in the Galapagos Islands in the Pacific.

ADULT (Fig. 51D, Plate IV D)
This species could easily be mistaken for *C.cardui*. The chief characters distinguishing it from the latter, however, are first, on the upper side, the submarginal row of five spots is very much more pronounced and two of them are much larger with blue centres. Secondly, on the underside, the submarginal row of spots is represented by two large eye-like marks only, instead of the five marks, two of which are eye-like but small.

Wing span is very variable. Measurements are recorded from 38 mm to 70 mm, but the average is about 50 mm.

EGG (Fig. 51A)
This is broadly ovoid, slightly tapering towards the top. A series of longitudinal ridges elongate towards the top where they become flange-like. The egg measures about 1.0 mm in height.

LARVA (Fig. 51B)
This is similar to that of the Painted Lady, *C.cardui*. The skin has a very dark velvety appearance with the branched spines light in colour. There is a lateral row of light coloured spots. It is about 40 mm in length when fully fed. In North America the larva feeds on the blunt-leaved everlasting, *Gnaphalium obtusifolium,* and various species of the closely related genus *Antennaria*. The larva forms a shelter by spinning a few strands of silk and folding a few leaves together.

PUPA (Fig. 51C)
This is similar to that of *C.cardui* and is about 24 mm in length. The pupal stage lasts about 9 to 14 days.

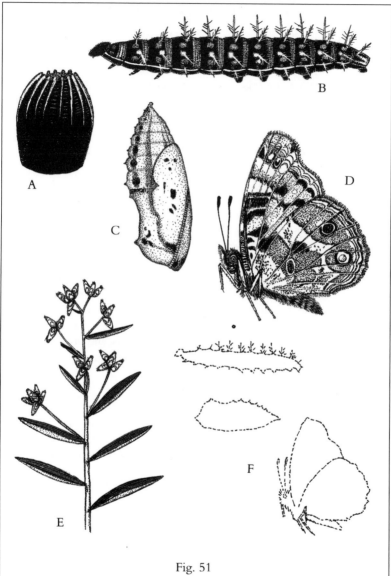

Fig. 51

American Painted Lady: A - Egg (ht. 0.1mm); B - Larva
(L 36mm); C - Pupa (L 24mm); D - Adult, side-view (wing-
span 50mm); E - Food plant: Blunt-leaved everlasting
Gnaphalium obtusifolium; F - Life size.

CAMBERWELL BEAUTY

Nymphalis antiopa (Linnaeus, 1758)

Only five records of this large, handsome migrant butterfly have been recorded from Ireland, mainly along the east and south coast. It is one of the most widely-distributed of all butterflies, being found throughout a large part of the temperate Northern hemisphere. However, it does not breed in Ireland; those found are thought to originate from Scandinavia where they are common.

ADULT (Fig. 52D, Plate IV C)
The male measures about 70 mm and the female about 76 mm across the outstretched wings. The ground colour of the upper wing surface varies from a rich, velvety ruby-brown to deep purple-brown. There is a broad, light straw-coloured band around the outer margins of all the wings and within this a blue-spotted, black band. This is so distinctive as to make for easy identification of the species.

The underside is also characteristic, with the outer margin similar to that of the upper side, but the rest of the wings is a dull brown, finely reticulated with black—resembling black lace, as in the Peacock butterfly. This species hibernates in hollow trees, dense brushwood, faggots, and similar situations. Severe winters appear to be beneficial to it. The following descriptions of the stages are based mainly on Frohawk (1924).

EGG (Fig. 52A)
Laid in batches in the spring on stems of willow, the eggs are fairly large. About 0.9 mm in height, they have 8 or 9 keels and, at first, are light brownish-yellow in colour, turning to olive-brown and then amber-brown, finally becoming reddish-brown and leaden.

The egg stage lasts about 19 days.

LARVA (Fig. 52B)
Frohawk, who had much experience in rearing this species from French stock, stated that the larvae will feed on sallow, willow, birch and elm. Feeding in colonies, they will cover the leaves and stems with a silk web, not separating until wandering away to pupate. The fully fed larva measures 54 mm in length and has pronounced intersegmental divisions. The ground colour is 'deep velvety black' and the head is bilobed. Except for the first segment, the whole body is covered with black spines, each bearing bristles. Starting from the third segment and continuing down the mid-dorsal line is a series of rust-red, shield-

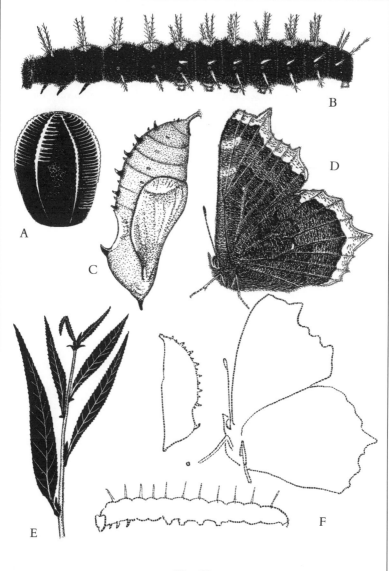

Fig. 52

Camberwell Beauty: A - Egg (ht. 0.9mm); B - Larva (L 54mm);
C - Pupa (L 25.5mm); D - Adult, side-view (wing-span m.70mm,
f.76mm); E - Food plant; Willow, *Salix sp.*; F - Life size.

shaped marks which terminate at the eleventh segment. The pairs of prolegs on segments six to nine inclusive are also rusty-red.

The larval stage lasts for about 30 days.

PUPA (Fig. 52C)

The pupa is about 25.5 mm in length and suspended by strong cremastral hooks to a silk pad spun in some suitable situation. The colour is very variable, but the dorsal spikes on the meta-thorax and the first two abdominal segments are most often surrounded by patches of a metallic hue—usually silver-gilt and varying much in size and intensity.

The pupal stage lasts about 21 days.

QUEEN OF SPAIN FRITILLARY

Argynnis lathonia (Linnaeus, 1758)

There are two records only of this rare immigrant in Ireland—one for Killarney, Co. Kerry, in August 1864 and the other for Cappagh, Co. Waterford, in September, 1960. It is a well-known migrant in Europe generally, as well as in Eastern Asia and North Africa. It often ranges far and wide. It is not indigenous, but occurs far more frequently in Britain than in Ireland.

In the southern parts of its distribution it undergoes two life-cycles in the year, but has only one in the north.

ADULT (Fig. 53D, Plate IV E)

Variable in size, 36 to 46 mm across the outstretched wings, the upper side of the wing is typically fritillary-like, being a rich, fulvous colour with the checkering of black marks. The shape of the forewing is characteristic, being more pointed (rather like the small male Silver-washed Fritillary), with the underside very distinctive with its pattern of large and small silver spots. The patches on the hindwing are quite a conspicuous feature when the butterfly is at rest—making it easily distinguishable from the other fritillaries.

EGG (Fig. 53A)

This is only about 0.6 mm in height (that of the Pearl-bordered Fritillary is about 0.7 mm), and is like a truncated cone in shape with the edges rounded. There are about 40 irregular ridges, of which only a proportion run the whole length of the egg. Each of these terminates in a small spike. When first laid, the egg is a very pale lemon-yellow but becomes greenish-yellow and, finally, leaden-grey. It hatches in about 7 days.

LARVA (Fig. 53B)

This is nearly 32 mm in length. The general ground colour is 'velvety black' and well sprinkled with white dots, each of which is furnished with a black bristle. The spines are brown and lighter at the base. A pair of white marks are to be found on the front part of each segment on the upperside. Greyish-brown marks are present on the sides.

The larval foodplant is wild pansy, *Viola tricolor*. There are continental records of various violet species as food plants. Larvae will, however, feed on the cultivated pansy.

The length of the larval stage is probably extremely variable, but little appears to be known about it. A long larval period going over the winter

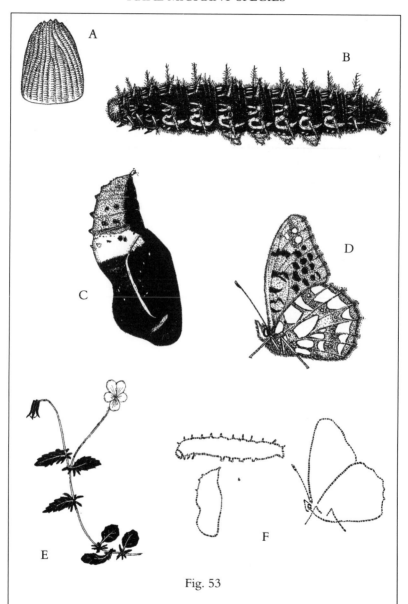

Fig. 53

Queen of Spain Fritillary: A - Egg (ht. 0.6mm); B - Larva
(L 32mm); C - Pupa (L 18mm); D - Adult, side-view (wing-
span 36-46mm); E - Food plant: Heartease, *Viola arvensis*;
F - Life size.

months may occur, or, on the other hand, depending on when the eggs were laid, it may be much shorter, perhaps 3 weeks.

PUPA (Fig. 53C)

Immediately before pupation, a large patch of silk is spun onto which the pupal cremaster is attached. The pupa measures from 17 mm to 19 mm in length, females usually being the larger. The head, thorax and wings are olive-brown, whilst the abdomen is speckled. The spiracles are black and prominent, but the most conspicuous feature (and characteristic of this species), is a band of pearly-white around the middle of the pupa, terminating on the margin of the wing-cases. In addition, there are small silver-gilt discs on the thoracic segments and on the first two abdominal segments.

MONARCH

Danaus plexippus (Linnaeus, 1758)

This very large butterfly, otherwise known as the Milkweed, or Black-veined Brown, is an occasional vagrant to Ireland. Ten are recorded up to 1964, but only one of these is in the National Collection; thereafter one is recorded in 1965, three in 1968, one in 1978, four in 1981, and one in 1985 (most records originate from Cork and Kerry).

It is a common North American species of well-known migratory habits. Multiple-brooded, it flies north in early summer and southwards in autumn.

The Monarch has reached many regions remote from North America. This could be due to (i) its ability to remain in adult hibernation and thus allowing it to been given an assisted passage in ships; (ii) it could have been blown off course during its long migratory flights; (iii) the possibility of its release from captivity cannot be eliminated.

The presence of the larval foodplant, however, is obviously a necessary prerequisite for its success in colonising any new locality. Only species of the genus *Asclepias* are eaten by the larvae, none of which is an Irish indigenous plant, although a few species are grown in gardens, albeit uncommonly.

The Monarch occurs in the Canaries and other Atlantic islands and this is a possible source of Irish specimens. It has recently been recorded as establishing breeding populations in Portugal and southern Spain.

ADULT (Fig. 54D, Plate IV F)
The Monarch is by far the largest butterfly on the Irish List. The single specimen, a female, in the National Museum, Dublin measures 113 mm across the outstretched wings. The ground colour of the wings on the upper side is brownish orange, but all the veins are heavily marked with black and there is a broad black band around the margin of all the wings, with the exception of the hindwings adjacent to the abdomen. This area also shades to a lighter, yellowish colour. Within the broad black band are two rows of spots of various sizes and white in colour. The underside of the forewings is much like that of the upper, but that of the hindwings is light brownish yellow. In the apical area of the forewings are seven larger white or light coloured spots.

The male can be distinguished by the presence of a prominent bar of black scales which cover the scent cell on vein 2 of the hindwing.

The flight of the Monarch is slow and flapping. It is distasteful to predators and a number of tropical butterflies mimic its colouration, thereby enjoying the advantage of being mistaken for the distasteful Monarch.

In North America the adult Monarch butterflies migrate in vast numbers

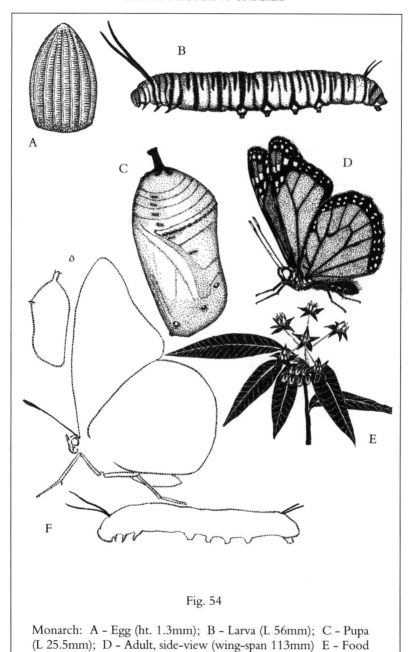

Fig. 54

Monarch: A - Egg (ht. 1.3mm); B - Larva (L 56mm); C - Pupa
(L 25.5mm); D - Adult, side-view (wing-span 113mm) E - Food
plant: Milkweed, *Asclepias sp.*; F - Life size.

and fly incredible distances to a few selected localities in Florida, Texas and Mexico. Here they hibernate, hanging in 'clouds' amongst the *Eucalyptus* and pine trees, often using the selfsame trees which their antecedents had selected.

EGG (FIG. 54A)

The egg is 1.3 mm in height and is, therefore, comparatively small for the size of the adult butterfly. (The height of the egg of the Small Heath is 0.70 mm but is said to be large for such a small butterfly.) Frohawk (1924) likens its conical shape to an acorn, but it is rather more pointed. There are from 20 to 23 longitudinal ridges, but only about 14 of these run the entire length from summit to base. There are about 34 transverse ribs and the micropyle bears a reticulated pattern. At first it is primrose yellow in colour but, before emergence, gradually becomes more leaden. The total length of the egg stage is about 90 hours, and the emerging larva eats away the crown of the egg in order to escape. Frohawk relates an incident of a young larva starting to consume another unhatched egg.

LARVA (Fig. 54B)

On emergence, the young larva is about 2 mm in length but after 4 moults (and fully grown) measures 56 mm. Except for the first and last tapering segments, the body is uniformly cylindrical. The yellow head has three transverse, black bands and the surface is sprinkled with minute, black hairs. Two long, fleshy, velvety-black tentacles arise from the second segment. These are densely clothed with extremely small points and sparsely sprinkled with fine, black hairs. They project over the head, slightly upturned and widely divergent at the extremities, and are constantly being jerked to and fro when the larva is feeding. There is a similar pair of tentacles (but much shorter) arising from the eleventh segment.

The ground colour of the larva is a pale lemon-yellow and white. The latter colour forming a band around each segment. There are two black bands on each of the segments from the fourth to the tenth and they extend over the back down to the spiracle, separating the white from the yellow—one anterior and the other at the posterior third. The bold colouration is probably a warning of unpalatability.

PUPA (Fig. 54C)

The pupa is about 25.5 mm in total length and is 12.7 mm at the middle of the abdomen—the widest point. The whole surface is smooth and rounded, with no projections except for the elongated stalk at the cremaster. Immediately after pupation the pupa is yellowish-green, but thereafter is a pale, glaucous-green with the appearance of jade. The posterior edge of the third abdominal segment is ornamented by a dorsal belt of brilliant gold colour on which are situated numerous knob-like protrusions. These are black and shining at the front edge, but like polished pearl reflecting the gold belt at the back. In addition there are six gilded spots running in an oblique band from the head to the posterior surface of the mesothorax.

The cremaster is also shining black and, in the centre of the top anal segment, there is a black spot with two small black spots also on the ventral surface. Black cremastral hooks attach the pupa firmly to the pad of silk. The white spiracles slightly protrude.

The length of the pupal stage is about 15 days.

EXTINCT SPECIES

SMALL MOUNTAIN RINGLET

Erebia epiphron (Knoch, 1783)

Whether this alpine butterfly still exists in Ireland is open to question, but it appears that it was last collected as long ago as 1901. E. Birchall is credited with the first specimen in 1854 'in a grassy hollow about half way up the Westport side of Croagh Patrick in Co. Mayo'. About 1901, W. F. de Vismes Kane found the butterfly on Mt. Nephin, also in Co. Mayo, and he also mentions a specimen 'believed' to have been taken on the hilly slopes on the eastern shores of Lough Gill in Co. Sligo in 1895. Almost every season, collectors have endeavoured to re-discover this butterfly but, so far, without avail. Elsewhere in Europe it has seldom been found below 460 m and its usual haunts are boggy areas, often remote.

It does, however, seem that this little butterfly is unlikely to have escaped the attentions of so many experienced observers over the years. Of the six specimens in the National Collection, only three can be said to be Irish with certainty. The Irish specimens are referred to by Warren (1948) as belonging to the subspecies *aetheria* ab. *nelamus*. In continental Europe this form is found in the Tyrol, Dolomites and the Swiss Alps.

ADULT (Fig. 55D, Plate IV K)
The general ground colour is drab, sooty-brown tending to grey towards the wing edges, whilst the fringes are grey. The expanded wings measure 35.5 mm across and they are patterned with a band of black spots, each surrounded by a rather hazy, tawny area which is indistinct, running parallel with the outer wing margin. In one Irish specimen the black spots are absent and the tawny area much reduced, whilst in another not only are the black spots absent but the tawny area is only just discernible.

NOTE: In view of the absence from Ireland today of this species, this account of the immature stages has been based on that of Frohawk.

EGG (Fig. 55A)
This is slightly less than 1 mm in height and stands on a rounded base. It is widest near the base but the crown is transverse with the micropyle in the centre. There are from 18 to 20 longitudinal ridges and the egg is finely ribbed transversely. Around the margin of the crown there are a number of angular projections. At first the egg is bright yellow but becomes duller and then speckled and blotched with a pale, reddish-brown. These markings darken into

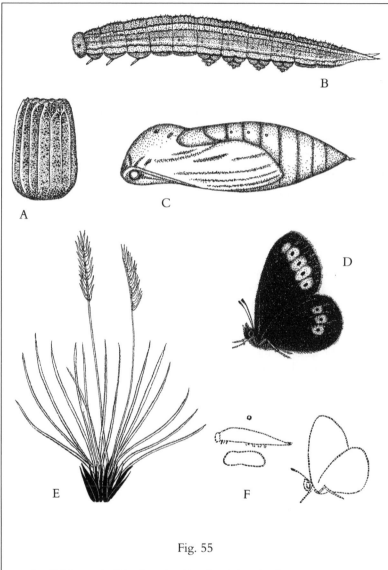

Fig. 55

Small Mountain Ringlet: A - Egg (ht. 1.0mm); B - Larva
(L 19mm); C - Pupa (L 10.5mm); D - Adult, side-view
(wing-span 35.5mm); E - Plant food: Mat grass, *Nardus stricta*;
F - Life size.

rust-red. Just before hatching the young larva can be plainly seen through the shell. 18 days are spent in the egg stage.

LARVA (Fig. 55B)
When fully grown, the larva measures about 19 mm in length, with the general body colour grass-green. The globular green head is roughly granulated and bears many minute, whitish bristles. The body tapers at each end—the fore end more abruptly—and the hinder end terminates in a pair of horns edged with a darker green line tinged with dull brown. There is a dark green, longitudinal stripe down the middle of the back, bordered with whitish-green. On each side of this stripe are two conspicuous dull-white stripes, the first of which is edged on each side by a darker green line, and the second contrasts with the darker green ventral surface. Midway between these two stripes is a fine, whitish-green line and there is another broader line of the same colour immediately below the spiracles. The latter are small and have a pale yellow blotch in front of each.

The whole body surface is granular and covered with minute, black, claw-like points, each arising from a pale spot. The young larva commences hibernation about the end of September and finishes about March. Frohawk found that the total larval period was about 288 days.

In nature the food plant is mat grass, *Nardus stricta,* but *Poa annua, Festuca glauca, Deschampsia caespitosa* and *Aira praecox* have all been recorded as being eaten whilst in captivity. The larva mostly feeds at night. It falls to the ground on being disturbed.

PUPA (Fig. 55C)
This is about 11 mm in length. In lateral view, the head is somewhat square at the front and the thorax is rounded. The abdomen is swollen in the middle. When viewed from above the head is truncated and the body slightly angular at the base of the wings, whilst the latter and the abdomen are uniform in outline. The general body colour varies from cream to yellow-green. In the former, the thorax and wings are pale-brownish with the abdomen cream or pale primrose-yellow. The head is slightly darker as in all colour forms. Except for the abdomen, the body is streaked with olive-brown and the antennae, proboscis, and eye are strongly outlined with the same colour. A streak extends along the middle of the back to the metathorax. The abdomen is speckled with olive and dusky spots, mostly running in longitudinal rows—the larger being on the underside. The thorax and abdomen are covered with minute spines, but cremastral hooks are absent as the pupa lies in a slight cocoon amongst grass stems loosely spun together. This stage lasts about 21 days.

HEATH FRITILLARY

Mellicta athalia (Rottemburg, 1775)

The reason for this species, and its status, appearing in a list of Irish butterflies relies entirely on Birchall (1865), who stated that it was abundant in Killarney, Co. Kerry. It has not been recorded since. Baynes (1964) says that this may well be an instance of an isolated colony dying out. Lavery (1989) excludes this butterfly from the Irish list, believing it had been recorded initially (by Birchall) in error.

The terrain is difficult to traverse and many expeditions have been mounted in recent years to re-discover it; none, however, being successful.

Could this have been an error in location in the first place? The mystery is still unsolved and no positive Irish specimens have been found in any collections. Altogether it can be looked upon as a doubtful record.

ADULT (Fig. 56D, Plate IV J)
This butterfly shows a resemblance to the Pearl-bordered Fritillary with its orange-brown or fulvous ground colour and black reticulate markings. In this species, however, there are darker markings and the veins are more heavily lined.

The expanded wings are about 40 mm across in the male and 44mm in the female. Occurring in Britain during June and July, it frequents clearings and edges of woodlands where common cow-wheat, *Melampyrum pratense*, is to be found. It is very local, although sometimes abundant.

EGG (Fig. 56A)
About 0.50 mm in height, it is pale, pearly-white in colour with about 26 longitudinal ribs. Laid in small batches on the larval food plant, the eggs become more yellowish nearer hatching.

The egg stage lasts about 16 days.

LARVA (Fig. 56B)
When fully grown it measures about 25 mm in length, having hibernated after the third moult when it was just over 3mm long. Most of the larval stage is spent in a small group under a canopy of silk. The ground colour is purplish-black but a speckled appearance is given by numerous small, white spots from each of which a black hair arises. The conical tubercles are white or light-amber in colour.

Besides cow-wheat, other plants have been recorded as food plants, such as ribwort, *Plantago lanceolata* and foxglove, *Digitalis purpurea*.

The larval stage lasts for about 10 months.

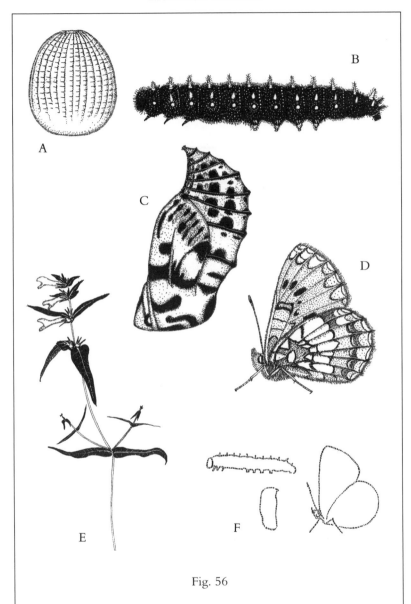

Fig. 56

Heath Fritillary: A - Egg (ht. 0.5mm); B - Larva (L 25mm);
C - Pupa (L 12.7mm); D - Adult, side-view (wing-span m.
40mm f. 44mm); E - Food plant: Common cow-wheat,
Melampyrum pratense.

PUPA (Fig. 56C)

Suspended by a cremaster furnished with numerous hooks, it is about 12.7 mm long, whitish in colour, tinged with light brown, and heavily spotted with black and orange.

This stage lasts about 15 days.

INTRODUCED SPECIES

LARGE COPPER

Lycaena dispar (Haworth, 1803)

The history of the Large Copper in Ireland has been dealt with frequently over the years by various writers including Ford (1945) and Emmet & Heath (1989). The following information on the introduction of this butterfly to Ireland is based mainly on Lavery (1990).

In 1913/14, about 400 adult ssp. *rutilus* Werneburg from Berlin, were released onto an especially created fen at Greenfields near Cappawhite, Co. Tipperrary, under the direction of E. B. Purefoy. This colony flourished until c.1930 when it died out.

A second colony, this time subspecies *batavus* (Oberthür) from Holland was established at Greenfields in 1926, surviving until 1937/38, and again from 1943-1954, the site becoming overgrown and no longer supervised.

ADULT (Fig. 57D, Plate IV G,H)
Colour photographs of male and female specimens as well as that of the underside of a male are shown on plate 28 of Ford (1945). Averaging 46 mm across the wings, the male is smaller than the female which measures 49 mm.

In general appearance and colouration the female upper side resembles the Small Copper, with the outer band of black spots in an arc. In the male the greater part of the wings is lustrous copper with two dark spots only on the forewings, and a dark, outer margin on both fore- and hindwings. In both sexes the undersides are similar and spotted as in the Small Copper, but the hind-wings are 'silvery-pearl-blue' with a broad, orange band near the outer margin.

It flies in July and August.

EGG (Fig. 57A)
Only slightly larger than that of the Small Copper, it measures 0.65 mm in diameter and 0.40mm in height. It is comparatively small for the size of the adult. Laid singly or in small groups, firmly glued onto the leaves of the food plant water dock, *Rumex hydrolapathum*, the egg is disc-like in shape, being flat at the top and bottom with convex sides. Around the micropyle is a ring of seven cell-like concavities and below this another ring of larger cells. Below this again, and around the 'equator' of the egg, there are a number of irregular cells.

Water dock is a native Irish plant found in ditches, marshes, or shallow water and is widespread in distribution, although rather rare. A colony of Large Coppers requires a high concentration of plants, and the eggs are usually laid on plants which are more or less covered by other vegetation.

The egg stage lasts for about 16 days.

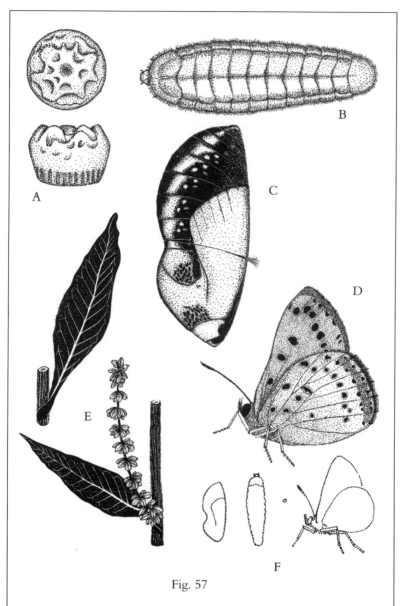

Fig. 57

Large Copper: A - Egg (ht. 0.65mm); B - Larva (L 20mm);
C - Pupa (L 12mm); D - Adult, side-view (wing-span m. 46mm,
f. 49mm); E - Plant food: Water dock, *Rumex hydrolapathum*;
F - Life size.

LARVA (Fig. 57B)

After hatching, the larvae soon hibernate amongst the dead leaves of the food plant and do not recommence to feed until spring, when young green leaves are available.

When full-grown the larva measures about 20 mm in length and is somewhat woodlouse shaped. The head can be completely retracted into the prothorax and claspers are not visible, being covered by the overlapping body. When viewed from the side, the dorsal surface is uniformly convex whilst the ventral surface is flat. The body is green with some obscure darker markings closely resembling the leaf on which it sits.

The larva can withstand extensive flooding. Like many lycaenids it is attended by ants and no doubt obtains some protection from this.

The length of the larval stage appears to be about 10 months. Frohawk, however, who acquired his three female adults from Hungary in early June, obtained a complete life cycle in under 7 weeks, and the larval stage lasted only 21 days.

PUPA (Fig. 57C)

The average length is about 12 mm and the width, at 6.7 mm, is over half this. Thus it is very stout in appearance, very rounded but with a blunt anal extremity. It is fastened to the food plant by cremastral hooks anchored to a silk pad. There is an intricate colour pattern in various shades of yellowish-brown, dark brown and 'buffish-white'. The spiracles are whitish and the whole body is covered with minute specialized hairs of various shapes.

The pupal stage is about 11 days in length.

LIST OF IRISH BUTTERFLIES

Common	Latin	Irish

RESIDENT SPECIES

HESPERIIDAE

Dingy Skipper — *Erynnis tages* ssp. *tages* ssp. *baynesi* — Donnán

PIERIDAE

Common	Latin	Irish
Wood White	*Leptidea sinapis* ssp. *juvernica*	Bánóg choille
Brimstone	*Gonepteryx rhamni* ssp. *gravesi*	Buíóg ruibheach
Large White	*Pieris brassicae*	Bánóg mhór
Small White	*Pieris rapae*	Bánóg bheag
Green-veined White	*Pieris napi* ssp. *britannica*	Bánóg uaine
Orange-tip	*Anthocharis cardamines* ssp. *hibernica*	Bánóg rinnbhuí

LYCAENIDAE

Common	Latin	Irish
Green Hairstreak	*Callophrys rubi*	Stiallach uaine
Brown Hairstreak	*Thecla betulae*	Stiallach donn
Purple Hairstreak	*Quercusia quercus*	Stiallach corcra
Small Copper	*Lycaena phlaeas* ssp. *hibernica*	Copróg bheag
Small Blue	*Cupido minimus*	Gormán bheag
Common Blue	*Polyommatus icarus* ssp. *mariscolore*	Gormán coiteann
Holly Blue	*Celastrina argiolus* ssp. *britanna*	Gormán cuilinn

NYMPHALIDAE

Common	Latin	Irish
Small Tortoiseshell	*Aglais urticae*	Ruán beag
Peacock	*Inachis io*	Péacóg

215

Pearl-bordered Fritillary	*Boloria euphrosyn*	Fritileán péarlach
Dark Green Fritillary	*Argynnis aglaja*	Fritileán dúghlas
Silver-washed Fritillary	*Argynnis paphia*	Fritileán geal
Marsh Fritillary	*Eurodryas aurinia*	Fritileán réisc

SATYRIDAE

Speckled Wood	*Pararge aegeria* ssp. *tircis*	Breacfhéileacán coille
Wall Brown	*Lasiomata megera*	Donnóg an bhalla
Grayling	*Hipparchia semele* ssp. *hibernica* ssp. *clarensis*	Donnóg aille
Gatekeeper	*Pyronia tithonus* ssp. *britanniae*	Geatóir
Meadow Brown	*Maniola jurtina* ssp. *iernes*	Donnóg fhéir
Ringlet	*Aphantopus huerantus*	Fáinneog
Small Heath	*Coenonympha pamphilus*	Fraochán bheag
Large Heath	*Coenonympha tuillia*	Fraochán mór

COMMON MIGRANT SPECIES

PIERIDAE

| Clouded Yellow | *Colias croceus* | Buíóg chróch |

NYMPHALIDAE

| Red Admiral | *Vanessa atalanta* | Aimiréal dearg |
| Painted Lady | *Cynthia cardui* | Áileánn |

RARE MIGRANT SPECIES AND VAGRANTS

PIERIDAE

| Pale Clouded Yellow | *Collias hyale* | Buíóg liath |
| Bath White | *Pontia daplidice* | Bánóg bhath |

NYMPHALIDAE

American Painted Lady	*Vanessa virginiensis*	Áilleán meiriceánach
Camberwell Beauty	*Nymphalis antiopa*	Bé na fallainge
Queen of Spain Fritillary	*Argynnis lathonia*	Fritileán niamhrach

DANAIDAE

| Monarch | *Danaus plexippus* | Bleacht fhéileacán |

EXTINCT SPECIES

SATYRIDAE

| Small Mountain Ringlet | *Erebia epiphron* | Fáinneog shléibhe |

NYMPHALIDAE

| Heath Fritillary | *Mellicta athalia* | Fritileán fraoigh |

INTRODUCED SPECIES

LYCAENIDAE

| Large Copper | *Lycaena dispar* | Copróg mhór |

BIBLIOGRAPHY

Baynes, E.S.A., 1950. Irish *Argynnis Euphrosyne*, Linn. *The Entomologist* 83:105-8

Baynes, E.S.A., 1964. *A Revised Catalogue of Irish Macrolepidoptera (Butterflies and Moths)*. Classey. Hampton, Middlesex.

Baynes, E.S.A., 1970. *Supplement to a Revised Catalogue of Irish Macrolepidoptera (Butterflies and Moths)*. Classey. Hampton, Middlesex.

Bierne, B.P., 1943. The Distribution and Origin of the British Lepidoptera. *Proc. R. Acad.* 49B: 27-59.

—— 1947. The Origin and History of the British Macrolepidoptera. *Trans. R. Ent. Soc. London.* 98: 273-372.

—— 1952. *The Origin and History of the British Fauna*. Methuen. London.

—— 1956. *An Annotated and Classified Bibliography of Irish Entomology*. Unpublished copies deposited with the libraries of the *R. Ent. Soc.* London.

Birchall, E., 1866. Catalogue of the Lepidoptera of Ireland. *Proc. Dubl. N.M.S.*, 5: 57-85.

Birchall, E., 1873. The Lepidoptera of Ireland. *Entomologists Mon. Mag.* 10:153-156.

Crichton, M., and Ni Lamhna, E., 1975. *Provisional Atlas of Butterflies in Ireland*. (Part of European Invertebrate Survey) 2nd Ed. Irish Biological Records Centre, Dublin.

Donovan, C., 1936. *A Catalogue of Macrolepidoptera of Ireland* (With Supplement). Burrow. Cheltenham and London.

Dowdeswell, W. 1981. *The Life of the Meadow Brown*. Heinemann Educational, London.

Emmet, A.M. and Heath, T. 1989. *The Moths and Butterflies of Great Britain and Ireland* Vol 7(1). Harley Books. Colchester.

Ford, E.B., 1945 and 1957. *Butterflies*. Collins. London.

Frohawk, F.W., 1924. *Natural History of British Butterflies* 2 Vols. Hutchinson. London.

Greene, J., 1854. A List of Lepidoptera hitherto taken in Ireland as far as the end of the Geometrae. *Nat. Hist. Rev.*, I (Proc. of Soc.): 165-8.

Haynes, R.F. and Hillis, J.P., 1990. Report on Migrant Insects in Ireland for 1989. *Ir. Nat. J.* 23:277-279.

Heal, H.G., 1965. The Wood White, *Leptidea sinapis* L. and the Railways. *IR. Nat. J.* 15:8-73.

Hickin, N.E., 1980. *Irish Nature*. O'Brien Press. Dublin.

Higgins, L.G., and Riley, N.D., 1970. *A Field Guide to the Butterflies of Britain and Europe.* Collins. London.

Holland, W.J., 1903. *The Butterfly Book.* Doubleday Page. New York.

Howarth, T.G., 1973. *South's British Butterflies.* (Based extensively on the classic by Richard South) Warne. London.

Hyde, S.E., 1977. *British Caterpillars and Butterflies.* Jarold. Norwich.

Kane, W.F. de V., 1901. *A Catalogue of the Lepidoptera of Ireland.* London.

Lavery, T.A., 1989. The Heath Fritillary (*Mellicta athalia* Rott.): Did it really occur in Ireland? *Bull. Amat. Ent. Soc.* 48:158-159.

Lavery, T.A., 1990. The History of the Large Copper Introductions. *Bull Amat. Ent. Soc.* 49:33-36.

Lavery, T.A., 1992. The Distribution of the Wood White, *Leptiolea supapis javernica* Williams, 1946 in Ireland. *Journal of Irish Lepidoptera.* 1:15-16.

Nash, R., 1975. The Butterflies of Ireland. *Proc. Brit. Ent. Nat. Hist. Soc.* 8 (2):69-73.

Newman, L.H., 1948. *Butterfly Haunts.* Chapman and Hall. London.

Newman, L.H., 1967. *Create a Butterfly Garden.* John Baker. London

Newman, L.H., 1968. *The Complete British Butterflies in Colour.* (Illustrations by Mansell, E.) Ebury Press & Michael Joseph. London.

Ni Lamhna, E., 1980. Editor. *Distribution Atlas of Butterflies in Ireland.* (European Invertebrate Survey) Third Edition. An Foras Forbatha. Dublin.

Oldroyd, H., 1969. Handbooks for the Identification of British Insects. Vol 9; Pt 4 (a) *Tabanoidea* and *Asiloidea. Royal Ent. Soc.*

South, R., 1906. *The Buttterflies of the British Isles.* Warne. London.

Stokoe, W.J., 1944. *The Caterpillars of the British Butterflies.* Warne. London.

Stovin, G.H.T. (Editor) and Stokoe, W.J. (Compiler) 1944. *The Caterpillars of the British Butterflies.* (Based on South, R., *The Butterflies of the British Isles*) Warne. London.

Thompson, G., 1980. *Butterflies of Scotland.* Croom Helm. London.

Warnecke, G., 1964. *The Young Specialist Looks at Butterflies and Moths.* (Translated by Goodden, R.C.), Burke. London.

Warren, B.C.S, 1948. On the Race of *Erebia apiphron* Indigenous in the British Isles. *Entomologist* 81:181-186.

Webb, D.A., 1977. *An Irish Flora.* Dundalgan Press. Dundalk. 6th revised Ed. (First Published 1943).

INDEX